"How dare yo[u]"

"You had no right!" Viola exclaimed. "If my husband were present, he would call you out, sir."

A glimmer of a smile surfaced. "I think not."

"He is hot-tempered and wildly in love with me."

"Of course. But I do not think he would call me out."

"Why not?"

"Because, sweet wife," he said, stripping off his mask, "behold your hot-tempered husband."

Clarice Peters was born in Honolulu, Hawaii, where she still lives with her husband, Adrian, a high-school principal, and her son, Jeremy. She has worked as an advertising copy writer, freelance curriculum writer, and substitute teacher. She enjoys golf and tennis, and has a weakness for Italian food.

Recent titles by the same author:

ROXANNE
THEA
THE FALSE BETROTHAL

THE ABSENTEE EARL

Clarice Peters

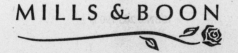

MILLS & BOON

For Shirley, Lynde and Peggy

MILLS & BOON, the Rose Device and
LEGACY OF LOVE are trademarks of the publisher.
Harlequin Mills & Boon Limited,
Eton House, 18-24 Paradise Road, Richmond, Surrey TW9 1SR
This edition published by arrangement with Harlequin Enterprises B.V.

© Laureen Kwock 1992

ISBN 0 263 79085 1

Set in Times Roman 10 on 12½ pt.
04-9506-66309 C

Printed in Great Britain by
BPC Paperbacks Ltd

CHAPTER ONE

NOW WHERE in heaven's name was her asp? Viola poked through the clutter of rouge pots, scent bottles and tortoiseshell hair brushes lining her dressing table, oblivious to her abigail's pleas to sit still.

"Miss Viola. I warn you, there will be no hair left for me to brush if you fidget so." Polly clicked her tongue and raked the brush through Viola's thick black hair. "I still don't see why you had Monique cut it so severely," she scolded with the ease of an old retainer.

Viola gazed absently into the gilt-edged mirror, jolted at her transformation this April evening in 1817 into a sultry siren of the Nile with soot-singed eyelids and a crimson mouth. Her usually unruly black hair had been trimmed severely at the ends, falling just below her cheeks and across her forehead. Monique had called it à l'egyptienne. It was very à la mode, and only the most sophisticated had the courage to wear it.

"You had such lovely hair," Polly lamented, mourning the butchering of her mistress's locks.

"It will grow back," Viola said, her hands continuing their search.

Botheration! There was still no sign of the small black snake she had placed in her reticule ten minutes previous. Had it wriggled out while she was getting dressed in her costume? She moved another bottle on her table. Duvane would be calling soon to escort her to Dorothea's party. She so disliked oversetting Polly, but she had to find her asp.

"Have you seen my asp, Polly?" she asked finally, driven to the wall.

Polly dropped the hairbrush. "Do you mean a snake, Miss Viola? The one what's poison?"

"Just a tiny one, Polly, and it's only a pretend asp. It must have crawled out of my reticule. Nothing to take a fright of," Viola hastily assured the older woman as Polly cast a frantic look about the floor of the dressing room.

"Perhaps it's under the furniture," Viola said, rising to search under first one and then the second cushion of the velvet settee across the room.

"Miss Viola. Stop that," Polly implored. "A fine sight you'd make if anyone saw you, looking for creatures that best belong in the garden. You will get your costume wrinkled before the masquerade even starts."

Viola paid no heed to Polly's entreaties, peering speculatively instead at the draperies. Perhaps the snake had crawled up there.

She was giving the linen draperies a vigorous shaking when Lady Susan Worthing strolled in.

"Viola? What are you doing!" she enquired.

Lady Avery turned to her sister-in-law with a smile.

"Oh, Susan. What a first-rate costume!" she exclaimed.

Lady Susan was indeed dressed in splendid fashion this evening as a nymph with green leaves sewn strategically about her gown. Her auburn tresses were curled and a garland of flowers placed on the top.

"Thank you, my dear," Susan replied. "I just called to see if you needed an escort to the masquerade. But since Charles and I met Duvane on the flagway, I know the answer to that already."

Viola knew Charles Worthing to be a most excellent gentleman, but he was unfortunately as horse mad as they came. If his Welshbreds were obliged to stand in the wind for long they might take a chill and he would never forgive her.

"You must not tarry on my account," Viola urged. "I am very late this evening. I know Charles will not like his horses to stand in the wind much longer. I shall follow in due time with Duvane."

Lady Susan hesitated.

"You cannot be thinking there would be anything untoward in Duvane's escorting me," Viola protested with a laugh. "Weren't you the very one who told me that it is *de rigueur* for married ladies to have *cicisbeos* and be escorted hither and thither by single gentlemen?"

Any answer Lady Susan might have offered to this remark went by the board because suddenly Viola spied a black snake slithering across her Wilton. Thoughts of *cicisbeos* flew from her brain as she pounded upon it. Polly shrieked and fled the room.

"I vow, Viola, I do believe you'll win the prize for the best costume!" Lady Susan crowed with laughter. "But mind you don't lose that reptile at Dorothea's ball. Bedlam will undoubtedly result."

"I'll keep it firmly in hand," Viola promised, popping the snake into her reticule and drawing the strings tight. "Now we can be off."

However, it was Lady Susan's turn to dawdle, standing by the doorway, just a hint of a frown puckering her brows.

"Is something amiss?" Viola asked. "Is it all this paint I am wearing? I know that it makes me look a fright, but I have to wear so much cosmetic because I am Cleopatra."

"No, my dear. It's your gown. It looks—"

"Ugly? Loathsome? Repellent?" Viola asked in turn.

"It just strikes me as rather plain."

Viola glanced at her reflection in the mirror. The gown was cut bare to the shoulders and the soft folds of white satin and silk were draped sedately down her front.

"It's lovely, to be sure," Lady Susan went on quickly, "but a jewel or two would bring it out even more."

Now Viola knew what game was afoot. "We've covered this ground before, Susan. I don't possess any jewels, except for my wedding ring." She stared down at the heavy gold band encrusted with rubies and diamonds which she wore on her left hand, remembering how one year ago exactly Richard had put it on her finger at St. George's. Her heart had been full to bursting with love for her handsome husband, the Earl of Avery. Then five hours later her world came crashing down on her shoulders.

The newly wed earl had bolted for the Continent, leaving behind a terse note in Viola's bedchamber.

"I fear I have made a mistake. My error. Not yours. Avery."

He had not communicated to her since then, except through his solicitor, Mr. Thacker.

For days Viola had wept, wondering what she could have done wrong. True, she was impoverished and without dowry, but Richard knew all that. She had never hidden the urgency of her family's situation from him. Her abandonment had been fuel for the prattle-boxes, though with Susan's help she tried to turn an indifferent face to Society, maintaining that Avery had always yearned to travel and was fulfilling this compulsion before they set up their nursery.

"The Avery heirlooms include a sapphire-and-diamond brooch which would look the very thing on that costume." Susan's voice summoned Viola from her brown study.

"You know my opinion on the Avery jewels."

"I know you must be the only woman in London with jewels of such quality who shows no interest in wearing them. They are Avery's. And you are his countess."

"A mere formality, Susan," Viola said, opening a perfume bottle and applying a touch to her wrists. "We needn't peel eggs about it. Everyone in London knows that a year ago today Avery married me and then bolted, never to be seen again. What is it that the wags call me? The Abandoned Countess? And they dubbed him the Absentee Earl."

"Pay no attention to those gossip-mongers." Susan shuddered. "I vow I wish Richard *were* in London. I'd wring his neck for what he did to you. Your own father must be furious."

Viola said nothing. Her father, Mr. Sidney Challerton, didn't care a fig about his son-in-law's comings and goings as long as the settlements had been made.

Nor had she sought comfort from her aunt, Mrs. Simmons, who'd raised her in Gloucestershire. Viola had learned years ago that the best way to deal with Aunt Simmons was to shrug and answer any of her querulous questions with a question of her own. A vacuous look on the face usually subdued Mrs. Simmons into speechlessness.

"Oh, Viola, I am sorry for prattling on this way," Lady Susan said, looking guilt-stricken. "Especially tonight of all nights."

"It's all right, Susan. I've grown quite accustomed to my silly situation."

At these words, Susan stared so closely that Viola wondered if she had done it too brown.

"And now, we must go," Viola prompted, "or Charles and Duvane will never let us hear the end of it."

Hastily recalled to the urgency of removing her husband's Welshbreds from standing in the night air, Lady Susan preceded her out the door. Viola was about to follow when she decided to check on the asp. As she put her hand into the reticule, her heavy ring caught against the snake's skin.

The poor creature. She brought it out again and examined it. Luckily no damage had been inflicted. But obviously she couldn't wear the wedding band to the masquerade and keep the snake in the reticule. Since she couldn't think of a hiding place for the reptile, the easiest solution would be to take off the ring. And yet could she?

Richard himself had put it on her finger. She had promised never to take it off. He had also promised to love and honour her, she reminded herself. Grimly, she twisted the ring off her finger and tossed it down on her dressing table.

AS THE IRON CARRIAGE wheels rolled over the cobblestone streets, Viscount Duvane, dubbed the Blond Adonis by the bow-window set, leaned back against the velvet squabs and dealt a quizzical eye at his companion, feeling a trifle put out. Duvane had had a difficult time discovering what costume Viola would wear tonight, finally forced by the exigencies of time to bribe Monique her hairdresser into divulging that she had just given the countess an Egyptian cut. Then considerably more of his time and energy had been expended ordering a costume as the Roman general Marc Antony to complement hers. Yet not a word of praise had she spoken.

Thinking of her dratted earl, no doubt.

"By all odds I should be angry with you, my lady," he said, breaking the silence which had fallen.

Viola, who had been staring out the window, looked over, astonished by his words. "Angry? What have I done to put you on end, sir?"

"A year ago you married Avery. If I had known you then, I would not have allowed any such thing."

"Do be serious. You could not have prevented my marrying Avery. My father approved the match. I wanted it. Avery wanted it."

"I would have won you, had we met then," he said with such confidence that she did not know whether to be flattered or appalled.

Duvane was acknowledged to be one of the ton's leading bachelors, strikingly handsome with a squarish jaw, aquiline nose and piercing blue eyes. He also showed a handsome leg, well displayed tonight in the dress of a Roman soldier complete with leggings and leather sandals.

He would have made a compelling rival to Avery, Viola thought before giving her head an abrupt shake. But no, he wouldn't have. She had never seen a more dashing man than Richard. Wholly enthralled by him, believing herself in love, she would not have looked at another man. She still wouldn't if her husband were in London instead of gadding about on the Continent.

"You have not commented on my costume," Duvane said.

"How remiss of me!" she exclaimed. "Indeed I meant to. A Roman soldier—quite authentic."

"Not just any Roman soldier," he protested. "A general. Marc Antony. To go with your Cleopatra."

"Oh, Duvane, how clever of you. Is that who you're supposed to be?" she asked lightly.

"Yes," he said, his smile faltering a trifle. "When I learned that you were to be Cleopatra I decided that I must go as Marc Antony. I am your *cavalier servant,* dear lady," he said.

Viola's laughter bubbled up. Duvane was a flirt, but thankfully, he never went beyond the limits of propriety. She found him an amusing companion, and it was a feather in her cap that he devoted himself to her, a married lady, rather than to the bevy of single females throwing out lures.

It was a dark night, a new moon making it difficult for the countess to discern the expression kindling in the viscount's eyes. Had a full moon shone, she might well have seen not amusement flickering in Duvane's blue orbs but cunning.

In truth Duvane had a profound dislike of the earl, a dislike which had originated two years previously in Buckinghamshire. After sustaining heavy losses at a house party, Avery had refused to play longer, saying that he wasn't certain if all the players were abiding by the rules. Although no names were mentioned, the comment was deemed to be aimed at Duvane since he was the chief winner.

It was an insult of the first order, and utterly false, to the viscount's way of thinking. It wasn't cheating, precisely, if one were foresighted enough to place an appropriate card up one's sleeve. Duvane had denied the charge and had even toyed with the notion of calling Avery out. Only the knowledge of the earl's superior skill with pistols and swords had dissuaded him.

Since the earl's influence was enormous, suspicion followed Duvane, and certain gentlemen deep in the pocket began refusing to sit down with him at the green baize tables. He had been obliged to eschew the cardrooms in London for over a year until he heard that Avery himself had quit London. He returned swiftly and worked his way back into the good graces of the other card-playing gentlemen. He also took every opportunity to provide succour to Avery's abandoned countess, a pretty enough chit. He had thought it would be a simple task to coax her into bed, thus wreaking the ultimate revenge on the earl, but the minx had shown no inclination to be bedded.

Yet tonight Duvane had noticed at once that the hand clutching her reticule so tightly was bare of any jewellery. Lady Avery was not wearing her wedding ring. Was his patience about to be rewarded?

DOROTHEA HAD CERTAINLY done herself proud in getting her Town residence ready for the masquerade, Viola thought as she stepped around a rose-bedecked Corinthian pillar fronting the Palladian edifice. In front of the door stood a huge bower of white and red roses through which fairy princes, woodsmen, centaurs and gnomes walked.

She paused a moment to adjust her mask then took the viscount's arm and joined the throng. Above her head a huge chandelier swayed to the rhythm of the lilting melodies drifting down the stairs from the ballroom.

She followed two wood sprites up the marble stairs, wondering if they could be Susan and Charles. So many nymphs and sprites flitted about tonight. There were also, alas, a good number of Cleopatras. Viola counted three Queens of the Nile since entering Dorothea's residence. So far all three were *sans* asps.

At the top of the stairs Dorothea, Lady Dixon, attired as a shepherdess, took the hand which Viola extended to her and stared hard at Viola's ringless left hand. The Avery ring was very distinctive. Had Dorothea been counting on that to aid her in identifying her guests? Hugely enjoying her friend's predicament, Viola passed unidentified into the ballroom, which was now crowded with twirling couples, the waltz being the current rage.

"May I?" Duvane held out his arms.

He was an excellent dancer, whirling her expertly in time to the music. Certainly better than Charles Worthing, who succeeded the viscount as her partner and who implored her not to have Susan dress him as a wood nymph ever again.

"Oh, Charles, you're not a nymph, you're a sprite," she said, swallowing a giggle. "It's quite different. And you look just the thing."

"Susan told you to say that, I wager," Charles said. He was a sandy-haired gentleman blessed with an open smile and generous disposition. Except for his partiality to his horses, he was a devoted husband, a fact which was made evident by the leafy costume he wore.

"How did you know I was the right Cleopatra?" she demanded.

"Didn't. I've already danced with three other Cleopatras. Susan wanted to be sure that you got here safely."

"Duvane is an excellent whip."

"Hmmph." Charles snorted. "Wasn't thinking of his driving."

Viola nearly trod on his foot. "Have you some reason to dislike Duvane, Charles?"

Mr. Worthing shook his head. "No, but I ain't a lady."

"Are you saying he's a rake?"

Charles's complexion turned a deep pink. "Well, really, Viola . . ."

"I recall talk that Avery himself was a rake before I married him." And for all she knew he still was!

"Wasn't the same thing at all," Charles protested as the music faded. A russet-haired nymph sidled up, demanding to know what Cleopatra and the wood sprite could be talking about.

"Actually, Susan, we were talking about your brother's rakish past," Viola said, recognizing Lady Susan at once.

"Oh, Charles, really." Susan rounded on her beleaguered spouse. "What a topic to pursue during a waltz."

"I didn't. Mum's the word. Didn't say a thing about his ballerina or that flaxen-haired creature he used to dote on."

"Charles!" Susan stamped her foot. "Why don't you go and see if Dorothea has set up tables for cards."

Charles hastily excused himself.

"Viola, you must forgive Charles."

"Heavens, there's nothing to forgive. I knew Avery was a rake before I married him, though I didn't know the particulars about the ballerina or the flaxen-haired creature. Were they very pretty?" she asked wistfully.

"No. Neither of them," Susan said with some confusion. "You cast them quite into the shade, particularly the flaxen-haired creature, who had a disgusting habit of taking snuff."

Viola laughed, not entirely reassured. She knew her looks were only passable. She was neither a Homely Joan nor a diamond of the first water. Avery could have married any other lady, one far more beautiful than she. But he had wanted her for a wife...if only for a few hours.

A rotund elf came up to her, demanding the next dance. From the elf Viola passed into the arms of an obese Bacchus who reeked of tobacco and tried to pinch her bottom.

She moved his hand quietly but firmly. A year ago she might have blushed and stammered but in twelve months' time, thanks to Susan, she had learned how to discourage such disagreeable advances.

She moved about the perimeter of the room, observing a Roman general deep in conversation with another Cleopatra. Was that Duvane, she wondered. She found her way past a cluster of young ladies standing with their mothers. These marriage-minded matrons could be heard adjuring their daughters to stop slouching, smile more and give over those die-away airs, lest they never catch a gentleman.

They sounded so much like her Aunt Simmons that Viola felt an immediate bond of sympathy for their young charges. A mere thirteen months ago she had stood in their shoes.

She shook off these thoughts and spied the refreshment room. As Viola started to enter the room, a Black Domino stepped in front of her, barring her way.

"Champagne, your Majesty?"

"Thank you," she said, taking the glass he offered her. He sipped his own drink.

"How is Egypt these days, majesty?" His voice was raspy, as though he was intent on hiding his identity, yet the warm timbre sounded familiar. Was he a friend of hers? He was quite tall and broad-shouldered and what she could see of his face not hidden by his mask was unusually bronzed from sun.

"Quite warm," she said, enjoying the pretence. "Which is why I came north to England."

His lips lifted in a half smile. "On your barge, of course?"

"Of course. That is an advantage of England being an island."

He chuckled. "Well met, lovely Egyptian. I confess I have always wanted to dance with a queen."

Intrigued, she accepted the invitation and put her champagne glass down on a nearby table.

A quadrille was forming, and they joined it, saying little to each other. At one point the dance brought them together and she felt his warm breath against her cheek. Her skin tingled. Who was he? He moved like a tiger, quietly and with grace, but with unmistakable power.

After the dance ended he escorted her to a chair in a quiet corner of the ballroom.

"You are flushed," he murmured.

"The exertions of the dance," she said.

"Pity. I thought it might be on my account."

She was taken aback. "Sir!"

She was even more outraged when he ran a finger across her cheek. She drew away, more furious than frightened.

"How dare you, sir!"

"Oh, I dare more, sweet Egyptian to whom so many have lost their hearts." He caught her wrist and pulled her to him, bending his mouth to hers.

He was going to kiss her! Alarmed now, Viola squirmed against him, beating against the solid, muscled chest with her fists, but it was no use. He was stronger than she. His lips pressed hers apart, stirring up forbidden desires. She mustn't. She couldn't. She wouldn't. *How dared he!*

Her reticule slipped down from her shoulder. *The asp.* Of course! As he planted kisses on the side of her neck and bare shoulders, her fingers worked feverishly to free the snake.

"Oh, sweet Egyptian, I have thought of you often," he whispered.

"Have you indeed," she murmured huskily, twining her left hand behind his neck while the right one triumphantly held on to the snake.

The eyes glinted with desire through his mask.

His head bent again to hers.

Now! Viola brought her right hand up and dropped the snake on his shoulders.

"Egad! What the devil!" he exclaimed as the snake slithered round his neck. Abruptly, he let go of her and shook the reptile off his body.

"Served with your own sauce, you despicable snake!" Viola exclaimed, her dark eyes flashing. "How dare you kiss me! Odious cur! You had no right!"

Black Domino stooped and picked up the snake from the floor.

"Did you really think this poor serpent would inflict a mortal wound on me, Viola?"

"All I wanted was to be out of your arms," she said coldly. Then she frowned as his words sank in. "You know who I am!" she exclaimed. "And you still tried to kiss me!"

"I didn't try to kiss you. I succeeded," he pointed out, now examining the snake with the help of a quizzing glass.

"If I were a man I'd call you out."

"But you're not, for which your husband must be thankful. What shall we do with this?" he asked, shaking the snake.

"If my husband were present tonight, he would call you out, sir."

A glimmer of a smile surfaced. He picked up her reticule and popped the snake back in it. "I think not."

"He is hot-tempered and wildly in love with me."

"Of course. But I do not think he would call me out."

"Why not?"

"Because, sweet wife," he said, stripping off his mask, "behold your hot-tempered husband."

CHAPTER TWO

JUST TWO HOURS earlier, Lord Avery had stood in front of his Berkeley Square residence, a look of befuddlement on his craggy face. The lock had been changed. Muttering a veiled oath, he withdrew his useless key and sounded the knocker. After a tiring trip across the Channel and an equally fatiguing ride from Bristol he wanted entrance immediately.

When several minutes passed and still no one responded, his annoyance had turned to anger. He rapped sharply on the oak door with his Malacca cane. Where the devil was Briggs? It was only nine o'clock. The fellow couldn't be abed already. Expelling an exasperated breath, the earl stepped back from the door and spotted an open window easily within reach.

Leaving his satchel on the front steps, he divested himself of his greatcoat and hoisted himself up the side of the building. He climbed quickly, hand over hand, until he reached the window-sill. He pushed the window and stuck his head in. Suddenly a Stentorian voice thundered in his ear.

"Stay put or I shall be obliged to shoot you."

Avery turned an august eye to the left and beheld his butler a yard away taking aim at him with one of his own silver-handled duelling pistols. No less astonished, Briggs blinked as he recognized the shaggy-haired intruder with the top half of his body in and the bottom half still dangling out of the window as his esteemed employer.

"My lord!"

"Put that weapon down, Briggs!" Avery ordered.

"Yes, my lord," Briggs said, following the instructions and dropping the pistol on the sideboard. "I beg your pardon, sir," he added hurrying forward to assist Avery over the window-sill and into the small breakfast room.

"Did you get him, Briggs. Did you get him?" James, one of the underfootmen, careened through the doorway, then gulped audibly. "Cor, it's himself."

"Yes, it is," Avery said, brushing dust off the sleeve of his white frilled shirt.

Ten years had Briggs served in the earl's employ, staring down tradesmen and undesirables and never having been put into a quake himself until this very moment.

Briggs cleared his throat. "Welcome home, my lord. It is good to see you looking so well."

Avery turned to the footman. "You will find my satchel on the steps outside, James," he said in a voice no less ominous for being quietly modulated, "also my coat."

"Yes, my lord." James, eager to be quit of the scene, departed.

"Before you dismiss me with ignominy, sir, I can explain," Briggs said with as much dignity as he could muster.

"I hope so," Avery said, stripping off his York tan gloves and going immediately to the tray of restoratives on the sideboard. "Is that my pistol, which I usually keep in my library desk?"

"Yes, my lord." Colour rose in the butler's cheeks. "Her ladyship gave me permission to use it."

The earl's blue eyes flickered as he poured himself a glass of claret. "Did she? And is it your habit to point it at every guest who might sound the knocker?"

"No, my lord. Just you. I mean, just this once. I beg pardon, my lord," Briggs said in strangled accents. "We didn't expect you."

Avery took a generous sip of the claret, pleased to find it even better than he remembered. His temper mellowed with yet another swallow. By the time the glass was empty, he had unbent sufficiently to find the incident amusing. It wasn't often that a gentleman was nearly shot by his butler, after all.

"This is prime, Briggs," he said of the claret.

"Yes, my lord. Her ladyship sampled it at Sir Thomas Kitteredge's and purchased several bottles at the Berry Brothers. She thought you would like it."

A connoisseur of spirits, was she? Avery wondered what other hidden talents his young wife of a year boasted. Then he shook his head abruptly. He didn't wish to dwell on Viola. He'd thought of her constantly during the year and now wanted to be done with such thoughts.

"Why are you pointing pistols at people?" he asked mildly. "And why was the front lock changed?"

"Since you were last in London we have had a number of burglaries in the square, my lord," Briggs said, now on firmer ground. "Lady Avery thought it best to change the lock and to prepare a plan in the eventuality that the burglars made an attempt here."

Amusement vanished from the earl's face. "Burglaries? How many?"

"Five or six in this past month alone. Lady Avery believes a band of thieves lurks nearby, watching to see owners leaving for a ball. They then descend to pick the place clean. Since she is out tonight we were being particularly vigilant."

"Vigilance is all well and good, Briggs," Avery acknowledged. "But why didn't you simply open the door?"

"That is a favourite tactic of the burglars, sir," the butler hastened to explain. "They ring the bell and when the door is open swoop in. So we left a window ajar and stationed ourselves up here whenever the doorbell rang at night so we could catch the thieves."

Avery rubbed the side of the cut crystal glass with his thumb.

"A highly original scheme."

Briggs brightened. "We thought so, my lord."

"Was it your notion?"

"Actually, my lord, it was Lady Avery's."

The earl paused, digesting this titbit. Viola, his country mouse of a wife, sampling his claret and now organizing his servants into an army? This didn't sound like the woman he had left behind.

"Just where is her ladyship? You said she was out. Is it her custom to keep late hours?"

"Her ladyship is attending a masquerade at Lord and Lady Dixon's. Lady Avery and Lady Dixon are quite bosom bows these days."

Avery mulled over this news carefully. Lady Dixon was part of the premier set in the ton. How had his wife found her way into that exclusive circle?

"Who went with her to this affair?"

"Lady Susan and Mr. Worthing. And Lord Duvane," Briggs divulged the last name reluctantly.

A quick frown descended on the earl's brow as he put down his empty claret glass on a silver tray.

He turned on his heel and stalked out of the breakfast room. Nothing sounded more tedious than the frolic of a masquerade just now, but it appeared that he must attend if he wished to speak to his wife.

Briggs hurried after him. "My lord, your rooms have been closed. Indeed the entire wing has been ordered closed by Lady Avery."

Avery whirled round so suddenly that Briggs nearly walked into him.

Her ladyship was entirely too free with her orders. The claret he would not quarrel with, but his private rooms! The gall of the woman, going on as though he no longer existed. Perhaps she had not anticipated he would ever return. It had probably suited her purpose well enough that he was absent. Well, he was back to queer her game.

"During this past winter a heavy snow fell, and the roof on the west wing was badly damaged," the butler explained. "That's why her ladyship ordered the entire wing closed."

"Has the repair been made?"

"Mr. Thacker was trying to contact you about it, my lord. I venture to say his letter never reached you."

"I shall consult with Thacker tomorrow and have the roof fixed directly. Which room is mine now?"

"You will be more than comfortable in the east wing, my lord," Briggs said, showing him the way. "Lady Avery's room—" he indicated the room Viola occupied. "You will find a fresh change of clothes in the wardrobe. I shall order your bath drawn."

Avery frowned.

"Why are you seeing to my bath, Briggs? Where is Walter?" he asked after his valet.

"Walter is no longer with us, my lord."

"Never tell me that her ladyship dismissed Walter!" Surely she wouldn't dare turn off his valet; that would be going too far.

"Oh, no, my lord. Indeed she implored him to stay. It was Walter's doing. Without you to dress, he sulked himself into a decline and saw no reason to be here. You know what pride he took in dressing you, my lord. He found a position with Lord Newton."

"Newton!" Avery exclaimed. His crony had been after Walter for a considerable time. "Blast! I shall just have to steal him back, shan't I? See if you can unearth that black domino I wore two Seasons ago."

"Very well, my lord."

Avery waited until Briggs descended the stairs, then he quietly turned the knob and entered his wife's private rooms. A fire burning in the fireplace gave a rosy hue to the darkened dressing room. He stepped over to the table, frowning at the assortment of cosmetics. She had never resorted to paint before. Why was she doing so now? Then he remembered: the masquerade, of course. As he picked up a bottle of scent, something caught his eye: her wedding ring.

She'd taken it off. His face was expressionless as he picked it up. A year ago he'd stood with Viola at St. George's, exchanging vows and placing this ring on her finger. Newton said he was mad. Viola Challerton was nothing like the out and outers he'd dangled after in the past. She was a veritable country mouse, almost Quakerish, due to her upbringing in Gloucestershire. However, something sparkled in her dark eyes, a hint of mischief which Avery found appealing. And although she could not hold a candle to the other Beauties, there was something about her lithe and trim figure which was alluring.

They'd met at a dreary Assembly at Almack's. He'd always thought to marry eventually, and a country chit whom he could school to do as he wished seemed the perfect answer. It was a simple enough task to win her heart. She seemed so grateful for his attention, with those violet eyes of hers brimming full of love. He'd half fancied himself in love, as well.

What a nodcock he'd been. Viola had never loved him. He had discovered that just hours after the wedding, as he strode past the blue drawing room. Hearing the voices of his new wife and her aunt, he'd stopped with a smile and opened the door a fraction of an inch to observe the two women.

"It's gone off exactly as we planned." Mrs. Simmons spoke from the couch. "Your father's saved from ruin."

"I hope for the last time."

"Avery made it plain that he won't have him hanging on his sleeve. He made the settlements. The man's besotted with you."

Viola smiled. Her aunt looked closely at her.

"Do you love him?"

In the doorway the earl waited confidently to hear her declaration of love. Instead his wife of four hours shrugged her pretty shoulders. "What is love?" she asked flatly.

Grim-faced, Avery turned away to the book room. A shrug. Was that all he merited from her? *"What is love?"* He knew she was shy, but Mrs. Simmons stood to her very much like a mother. She'd tell her aunt if no one else.

His pride had suffered a mortal blow. She didn't love him. She was nothing but a fortune-hunter out to save her blasted father. But those eyes of hers—they adored him. Adored his money, more likely. He'd picked up a quill and dipped it in ink. Scarcely knowing what he was writing, he'd scrawled a message and signed his name. Then he'd left the house.

AVERY HAD RETURNED. Viola stared dumbfounded at her absentee husband. All the speeches she had rehearsed during the year withered on her tongue. His face looked very brown, doubtless a consequence of his travels in the Mediterranean, and his hair was worn too long to be fashionable. Her gaze drifted up his tall, lanky figure. He appeared thinner. Perhaps the food on the Continent was not as good as it was rumoured to be.

Thin or not, he was still as handsome as ever, with an aquiline nose and chiselled jaw. His blue eyes were as piercing as the Atlantic, and held such cool amusement that she felt a flicker of anger flit through her again. So he thought it funny, did he? Leaving her on the day of their wedding and not returning for a year was just a jest to him.

"Have you nothing to say to your husband?" he quizzed.

"You're very brown, and your hair is too long," she blurted out.

This greeting surprised a crack of laughter out of him.

"So I am," he agreed. "India's sun is scorching. You would burn that exquisite countenance of yours to a crisp. At least I assume it is still exquisite under all that paint.''

''Thank you, my lord. No doubt it was concern over my complexion which compelled you to leave me behind.''

The earl felt the sting of her words. So his country kitten had grown claws in the year past.

''I didn't intend to stay away a year,'' he said truthfully.

''Have you been gone that long, Avery? I scarcely noticed,'' she said, affecting an unconcern she was far from feeling.

He lifted an eyebrow. ''Well, I certainly noticed the changes in my household. You have had a free hand with things, my lady. Ordering my claret, giving my butler permission to use my pistols, concocting that bacon-brained scheme to thwart the burglars. Briggs nearly blew my head off.''

''Oh, did he?'' Viola said eagerly.

''You needn't look so pleased.''

''I'm pleased only because it meant that the scheme worked. So it can't have been so bacon-brained, after all.''

The justice of her words did not soothe his ruffled feathers.

''Someone had to take things in hand, my lord,'' she continued. ''You were absent.''

''Mr. Thacker has always attended to matters for me satisfactorily.''

"Mr. Thacker fell ill with rheumatic fever twice this year."

The earl was shocked. "By Jupiter, I knew nothing of this."

"How could you, my lord? You were away."

"I know I was away," he said irritably. "How is Thacker? When was he last ill?"

"During the winter. He's much improved."

"Thank God. Who else was aff..cted?"

Her lips tightened momentarily. "No one of importance to you, sir."

"Good. Briggs told me that you ordered the west wing closed."

"The roof was leaking. I did not think you wished to come home to find your rooms ruined." She was growing annoyed. He hadn't seen her in a year and offered no apology for his absence, not a word of explanation. All he did was quiz her about mundane household matters.

"The roof has never leaked before."

"And therefore you suppose it never can?" she asked, incensed by his words.

Avery peered into the stormy eyes. He'd never seen her angry before, he suddenly realized. She certainly looked different from the Viola of a year ago. That was probably owing to her costume.

She was paler than he remembered and her hair, which had been long and lustrous, had been hacked off. Her violet eyes were her most brilliant attribute, and instead of gazing demurely at him they were flashing lightning bolts through soot-singed lashes.

So the fortune-hunter was angry, was she?

"Good heavens. Richard!" Lady Susan exclaimed as she passed on the arm of Mr. Worthing. She threw herself exuberantly on her brother's chest.

Viola watched them with a touch of envy, an emotion which turned to astonished delight when Susan stepped back and delivered a ringing blow across her brother's right cheek. As good a facer, Lord Dixon later declared, as had ever been delivered by Gentleman Jackson himself.

"Good Lord, Susan!" Charles, a bewildered onlooker to this act of violence, pulled his wife to one side. "Are you all about in the head? You've drunk too much champagne. Richard, I apologize."

"I don't!" Susan declared defiantly.

"Pray, don't disturb yourself, Susan," her brother said, rubbing his cheek before putting his mask back on. "Your blow was almost civil compared to Viola's greeting."

"What did you do to Richard?" Lady Susan asked her sister-in-law.

"I dropped my asp down his back," Viola replied, her lips twitching at the memory.

"On my shoulders, to be more precise," Avery said. "Add to that my butler nearly shooting me with my own pistol when I entered my residence and it's enough to compel me to depart for India again."

"India? Is that where you were? How did you get so far?" Susan demanded, cutting into the earl's litany of complaints. "What was it like? Speak, Richard, or I shall box your ears again."

"I found it devilishly hot, and I don't recommend it to you. The scorching sun would coarsen your complexion. I said as much to Viola."

"But how did you get there?" Charles asked.

"I fell in with the Sherwood brothers. You remember them, Sue, don't you? The twins who lived in Warwickshire."

Lady Susan nodded. "Their father went bankrupt. What happened to them?"

"I met them in Paris. They were on their way to Italy. From Italy we went to Albania. And from there to Greece. From Greece it was a short hop to Constantinople. And then since I was halfway to Asia the brothers insisted we see India."

"Did they return with you?"

"No. They remain behind with the cows."

Susan choked. "What cows?"

"There are cows on every street in Delhi, my dear sister. The Indians believe the cow is sacred. Hence none are ever slain for food. The animals are free to roam, to stand where they wish, to lie down where they please."

"Can't you hit them to make them move?" Charles asked.

"Of course. But then the Indians would hit you."

"I can see why you were eager to return home," Susan said, rearranging her garland, which was in danger of falling off her head. "You've always abhorred fisticuffs."

"It was not so much eagerness as necessity," her brother replied.

His words fell on Viola like a hammer. No, of course he wouldn't be eager to return to London. *She* was in London, after all. It had been necessary to return; a year was a long time. But no doubt after he put his affairs in order he would be off again—without her. She swallowed hard.

"My lady Cleopatra, your Marc Antony has been hunting for you everywhere." Duvane appeared at her elbow.

"La, sir, you know that searching is half the fun." Viola turned to him with relief.

Duvane smiled at the others in the group. "Pray, excuse us, Cleopatra has promised to take supper with me."

"I think not," Avery drawled.

Duvane chuckled and wagged his finger at Viola. "You have made another conquest, my lady, but one who does not know his place."

"And what place is that?" Avery asked dangerously.

Duvane tossed his blond head back in a manner which usually made susceptible females swoon. "Behind all her other admirers."

"And who is first among her admirers?"

"I am, of course," Duvane said.

"Is that so, sweet Egypt?" Avery asked, one finger caressing Viola's chin.

The viscount took instant exception to this familiarity. "How dare you, sir!"

Viola thought it best to intervene.

"Duvane, pray don't do anything foolish, such as flinging your glove in his face," she said with a languor she was far from feeling. "I have already told Avery that his jest is ill-timed. To descend on us in this wayward fashion is the outside of enough, but what can I expect of a husband who insists upon travelling round the world. Susan agrees, do you not?"

"Oh, yes, with my whole heart," Lady Susan said, rising to the occasion. "And so you see, my lord, why we must needs adjourn to the refreshment room to discuss pressing family matters. You will excuse us, won't you?"

"But of course." The viscount bowed, staring very hard at Avery. "Family matters."

While Lady Susan recounted all the London news to her brother, Viola chewed on a lobster patty, wondering if Avery had even an inkling that his abandonment of her a year ago had been the leading on-dit until Sir John Saffery's byblow had suddenly appeared in London. After that, Viola had always had a soft spot in her heart for the ancient Sir John.

Avery ate heartily of everything, explaining that he had tired of the curries for which India was famed.

"They are so hot that they would fry your tongue and innards."

"Then I shall order Cook to prepare a bowl of gruel for you tomorrow morning, sir," Viola murmured.

Susan chuckled and rose to refill her plate. Charles followed. Avery's plate was empty, as well, but he remained seated at table with Viola.

"You are not hungry," he said, pointing to her plate.

"I have not been in India, frying my innards."

He laughed, amused to hear his words from her lips. Two other Cleopatras drifted by in the company of a chubby Nero.

"How did you know which Cleopatra I was?" she asked, puzzled by how swiftly he'd recognized her. "Unless you subjected the other Cleopatras to your kisses."

"No, dear wife, I did not inflict my brutish kisses on the other Egyptian queens. It was quite simple, really. Polly described your costume to me in exhaustive detail." He grimaced. "She neglected to describe the snake. Was that intentional, I wonder?"

"She didn't see the snake," Viola said. "She ran screaming from the room. The poor creature is probably still quaking."

Recalling the severe looks from his wife's abigail, Avery remained silent.

"Why did you return, Avery?" Viola asked quietly.

It wasn't the question she wanted to ask. Why had he left—that was the puzzle which had tormented her all year.

"To wish you happy anniversary, my dear," he said, touching his glass of champagne to hers.

She flinched from his words. "Happy anniversary." But they had no marriage to celebrate, no year of happy events to look back upon.

"Thank you," she replied.

"I even brought you a present, one you've received before."

Puzzled by these cryptic words, she stared across at him. He held out her wedding ring between his thumb and index finger.

"I hope you don't make a habit of leaving this on your dressing table every time you go out," he said. "You may mislay it."

"Thank you, my lord," she said and started to take it.

"Allow me." Gently he slipped the ring onto her finger, just as he had done on the day of their marriage. Viola's hand trembled. A year ago she had been cast in alt; now it was all a mockery. What a peagoose she was. She blinked and, unable to look into his eyes, glanced off in another direction.

"There; that is much better, don't you think?" he asked.

"Thank you, my lord."

She wasn't looking at him, but over his shoulder. The earl, glancing in that direction, noticed Duvane had come in. Had she favoured that Captain Sharp with her attentions in his absence? If so, he'd put a stop to it at once.

Avery rose from his seat. "I think it time we went home."

"But it's not even twelve," she protested.

"I own to considerable fatigue."

"I wonder, then, that you did not stay at home, sir, rather than drag your weary bones to this masque."

His eyes glinted appreciatively. "I was anxious to be reunited with you."

"Prettily said, Avery." *And totally false,* she added silently.

"Lady Avery, I have come for my waltz," Duvane broke in at this point.

"Alas, my wife has no more waltzing in her for this evening," the earl announced before Viola could utter a word.

The viscount frowned. "I have never known Lady Avery to leave a ball before one of the clock. If you are fatigued, I will be glad to escort her home. I did bring her to the masquerade."

"You may escort yourself to Jericho," Avery said coldly. "I will not have you dangling after my wife." So saying, he took Viola by the elbow and propelled her towards the door.

Duvane watched the couple depart with a smile playing about his lips. How edifying to learn how easy Avery was to provoke when it came to his young wife.

CHAPTER THREE

As AVERY'S CARRIAGE bowled along the streets leading to Berkeley Square, Viola realized that this was their first opportunity to be alone as a married couple. After their wedding a year ago, so many people had besieged them, including her aunt Mrs. Simmons.

Viola shuddered now, remembering the struggle to extricate herself from that last interview with her aunt who, judging from the distasteful look on her face, felt obliged to inform Viola of the duties required of a wife in a bedroom.

Fortunately Mrs. Simmons turned cat in the pan and merely rambled on disjointedly about her niece's good fortune in landing such a matrimonial plum as the earl. All Viola had been obliged to do was to toss off a careless rejoinder and plant a vacuous smile on her face before her aunt tired of the charade and let her go.

The carriage stopped abruptly and Viola, who hadn't been paying much heed to their progress, was flung forward and then back into the protective circle of the earl's arm.

"John Coachman seems to have forgotten how to handle the reins," Avery said with a frown. His clasp was warm as he handed her out of the vehicle.

Briggs opened the door before she could take out her key.

"No weapon this time, Briggs?" Avery drawled.

"No, my lord."

Viola accepted the lit taper the butler handed her and turned to wish Avery good-night, but he took her by the arm and escorted her to the marble staircase. With trembling legs, she mounted each step. Would he seek entrance to her bedchamber, she wondered, her fingers trailing on the polished bannister. Alarm and anticipation warred within her breast. She darted a quick look at the gentleman at her side. He was her husband, after all; she could not refuse him.

He paused at her chamber door.

"Good night, my lord," she murmured and lifted her gaze to his face.

His strong, mobile mouth quirked in a smile. "Sweet dreams, sweet Egypt." He bowed and then moved towards his own bedchamber.

Disappointment and relief coursed through Viola's veins, then she shook off both emotions and retreated to her private rooms. No sooner had she closed the door and put the taper down than Polly, dozing on the settee, awoke and immediately set to work helping her mistress undress and remove the layer of paint on her face.

"Lord Avery's back," Viola murmured, feeling she would burst if she didn't speak to someone. Polly had known Viola since she was a lonely girl in the Simmons household.

Polly snorted and dipped a handkerchief into a basin of water. "I know. We spoke."

Viola gave her abigail a searching look. "You told Lord Avery that I was Cleopatra tonight, didn't you, Polly?" she asked.

Polly's usually cheerful face turned dour. "I had no choice, Miss Viola. He asked me straight out. There's nothing I would love more than to give him a rare trimming, but he'd as soon turn me off as look at me."

"He wouldn't dare. You are my abigail," Viola protested.

A knowing look came into Polly's grey eyes. "Aye," she said sadly, "but he is your husband first. He could dismiss me and there would be naught you could do about it."

Viola frowned, mulling over this piece of unanticipated information as Polly finished with her toilette. Her abigail was right. As her husband, Richard could do whatever he wished to her servants and to her. What a dolt she had been to have yearned for his return during the past year.

"He found you then without any trouble?" Polly asked, patting Viola's face dry with a linen cloth.

"Let us just say that he found me," Viola replied. She peered into the oval mirror in front of her, recognizing the waif with too large eyes and no colour in her complexion. As for that daring Egyptian cut—she sighed and consoled herself by thinking it would probably grow back by the time Avery was jauntering off somewhere else.

Polly shook the Cleopatra costume out, then picked up Viola's reticule.

"If you still have that snake in there, Miss Viola, the reticule's surely ruined. Why won't you let me have the footman put that creature back where it belongs in the garden."

"Very well, Polly. See to it, won't you?"

"At once, Miss Viola. Good night." Polly departed, carrying the reticule at arm's length.

A flannel night-gown had already been laid out on the bed. Viola slipped it over the thin cotton chemise she still wore. Sleep seemed far away, particularly with Richard in the adjoining chambers.

He was back, after a year's absence and without a syllable of apology or explanation. But did that matter? What husband ever fully explained anything to his wife? She could count on one hand the number of happy marriages she knew among the ton. That was one reason she had fought shy of all Aunt Simmons's schemes to marry her off. Only the urgency of her father's precarious finances had compelled her into marriage.

No, that wasn't entirely true. Her father's gaming debts had compelled her only to consider marriage, but she wouldn't have married just anyone. Her mind had been set quite firmly against matrimony until the night she had seen Avery, leaning against a wall in the Assembly Rooms, arms crossed, staring at her. He looked vaguely bored with the festivities. She had studied him openly, amused at the lures the other ladies threw out.

When he crossed the room and asked her to dance, she had been shocked to find herself accepting.

Would he want to visit her tonight?

Perhaps he had parted company from her at the door only to allow her time to ready herself for him. Her heart quickened, and she smoothed the flannel nightgown. The fabric was warm and comfortable but hardly alluring to a gentleman. She couldn't help thinking of the nightgown of white Norwich lace she had packed in her trousseau and never worn.

Well, she certainly would not dig it out for him tonight. If he wanted her he'd find her in flannel.

She drew the curtains around her bed and lay back, conscious of the pounding of her heart and waited.

And waited.

When the case clock in the hall sounded the two o'clock hour, Viola rolled over and buried her face in the goose-down pillow. What a ninnyhammer she was. Avery wasn't coming to claim her as a husband. It didn't make a jot of difference to him if she wore flannel or sackcloth to bed. For some reason he found her wanting. He'd found her so a year ago. He found her so now.

As THE FIRST RAYS of sunlight filtered through the bow window of his bedchamber, the earl stirred. From the nether world of his imagination came the scattered fragments of a dream—another one about Viola. He groaned. It was entirely too lifelike for comfort's sake.

This one had to do with her wedding ring. She was smiling like a sphinx at him and explaining how she had given the ring to Duvane for safekeeping.

Avery awoke with a jolt. *Viola. Wedding ring. Duvane.* The images revolved in his mind like a carousel. He sat up, shaking his head to clear it. *Odd, that dream.* Then he remembered the masquerade. The dream about Viola was based on fact, but still a dream like all the others which had plagued him during his travels.

What a gudgeon he'd been to kiss her so ardently after their dance last night. He hadn't planned to identify himself to her. He had merely wanted to feel her in his arms and peck her gently, but he had given in to his devil and kissed her, unprepared for the sweetness of her mouth.

He scowled.

Only with the most Herculean of efforts had he held his passion at bay at the door of her bedchamber. He knew he had every right to enter her bed; he was her husband. But he would not! She was a fortune-hunter, a liar and not fit to be the mother of his children.

He reminded himself sternly of these defects as he stood at the basin splashing water onto his face. It was too early to be up and about. In Town his habit was to rise at eleven and not a minute before, but he dared not risk sleep and another dream about her.

He didn't even have Walter to shave him.

He had just finished wiping the blade of his razor clean when Briggs knocked and entered.

"My lord, you are up earlier than your usual."

"I know." Avery patted his face with a towel. "But what are you doing here, Briggs?"

"I thought your lordship might need assistance in dressing. I am not entirely familiar with the role of valet, but James—" he prodded the other man standing at his side "—says that he would like to try."

Avery eyed him. "You fetched my satchel last night, didn't you, James?"

"Yes, my lord. I've watched Walter in your rooms on many an occasion and can do the job, sir."

Avery handed him the towel. "We shall see. For now, I think I shall contrive to dress myself. I've been doing it most of the year without assistance. You may watch, if you like."

"Thank you, my lord."

An hour later, Avery gazed into the pier glass. No one seeing his tall exquisite person would have suspected that he had expended considerable energy trying to tie a creditable Mathematical, spoiling three linen cloths in the process and dispatching James to find a fourth. He couldn't fathom it. His fingers had never failed him before, particularly when he wanted to look his best.

For her?

Certainly not; he squelched that errant thought immediately and with such a frown that James, holding out the coat of olive superfine, wondered if he had committed a solecism.

The earl thrust one arm into the sleeve of his coat, which was a year old but still serviceable. A frilled white shirt, biscuit pantaloons and Hessians polished to an eye-blinding gloss with a mixture of shoe black and champagne completed his attire.

In languid fashion, he left his bedchamber and descended the Adam staircase, making his way to the breakfast parlour where he was surprised to find Lady Avery quietly breakfasting alone.

To judge by the relaxed manner with which she perused the papers at her elbow, Viola had not heard his approach. Instinctively, Avery put up his quizzing glass. Seeing her last night as Cleopatra had not prepared him for this vision of her: dark hair pinned back to reveal a slender throat, and eyes that captivating hue of violet which of times made him think he was drowning in the night sky. Her complexion must be the creamiest in the kingdom and matched the simple but elegant ivory-coloured muslin she wore.

His lordship felt a desperate longing for . . .

"Coffee, damn it," he croaked.

Viola turned at the sound of the petulant voice. Her brows flew up. What was he doing up and about? She had hoped to have a quiet hour to look over the household accounts and think about her future. Polly had been in a frenzied worry, unable to sleep for fear that Avery would discharge her. Viola resolved to speak to Richard about that. And here he stood: her husband, roaring like an angry Vesuvius.

She hurried to pour him a cup from the urn at one end of the table and watched to see if the hot brew would calm him.

"Ah, much better," Avery said, feeling rather a fool.

"Good. I trust you slept well?"

"As well as could be expected." Considering that she was separated from him only by a wall, he added silently.

She rang a bell and a footman whisked in with a bowl of gruel.

The earl eyed it with acute misgivings.

"What is this?" he asked testily.

"You did say last night that Indian food fried your innards and you longed for a soothing gruel," she reminded him.

"Take this away," he muttered to the footman. "And bring me a plate of real food."

Viola hid a smile as the footman retreated to the kitchen. A plate of kippers, ham and shirred eggs was more to Avery's taste, and he ate with relish. Not so Viola, who merely toyed with the food at the end of her fork.

"You should eat more," he said now, blotting his mouth with a napkin.

"Breakfast is my least favourite meal. I usually take a tray in my room."

"However, this morning you came below and graced me with your presence? I'm honoured. Now that I think of it, you scarcely touched a morsel of food last night at the Dixons'. Perhaps your loss of appetite should be investigated by a physician, or is it only in my presence that you lose it?'' he quizzed.

"You have nothing to do with it," she said.

"I'm relieved to hear that. I'd hate to have you wasting away to skin and bones.''

"As you can plainly see, I am no such thing. I hope this will allay your fears. See?'' She lifted her fork and swallowed a slice of ham.

He certainly had seen the luscious lips open to take in the food and the long slender throat swallow it down. With the greatest effort he reapplied himself to his plate.

"What's that you have there?'' he asked, gesturing to the pile of papers near her plate.

"The household accounts, my lord. I thought to glance through them over breakfast. Since we now speak of household matters, perhaps this is the time for me to discuss your snuff.''

"My *what?*'' he demanded.

"Snuff,'' she answered and pantomimed taking a pinch between her fingers and inhaling.

"I am quite aware of how to take snuff, madam,'' he said icily. "I have been doing so for years. What about it?''

"I fear it has lost its potency as so many things do after a year's disuse,'' she said, blandly meeting his eyes. "Mr. George Berry has your standing order and was eager to replace your mixture, but I forestalled him. I had no notion you would be returning any time soon.''

"I shall replace my snuff this morning." He paused. "You have settled into my household uncommonly well, have you not, Viola?"

She poured herself another cup of coffee, returning his gaze with composure. "I had very little choice, my lord. You chose to go jauntering off to India. I was obliged to see to the running of things here in London."

"You spent all year here in London?" he asked incredulously. Was she mad? The cost of the upkeep alone...

"Certainly not. I am no henwit, sir, and rest assured you have not been reduced to penury. I spent the summer in Bath and Brighton."

Brighton! No doubt in one of those cheap lodgings far from the sea.

He pushed his empty plate away. "I trust you enjoyed yourself there. Did you perchance see Prinny bathing in the sea?"

Viola's laugh rang out. "Heavens, no. I don't think he even goes out in public any more. He is unpopular on account of the expense for his Pavilion. I saw it. And a more nonsensical building I have ever laid eyes on, though I daresay *you* would approve of it."

Avery, whose views of architecture bordered on the classic, was not about to accept this verdict.

"I would like that idiotish jimblejamble? Explain yourself."

"It has the look of India, sir," she said innocently. "Indeed in design it is probably more Indian than the buildings you saw in your travels. As for your question about the Regent's bathing, I don't think he bathes in the water any more because he has grown prodigiously fat and is forced to wear a Cumberland corset. I did meet his brother, the Duke of York, at a party given by the Bishop of Bath.''

''Really? How came you by the introduction to the Bishop of Bath?'' The bishop was a high stickler, if memory served Avery correctly, not about to recognize just anyone.

''His daughter, Aurora, was a friend of Lady Susan's. Aurora was kind enough to invite me to tea one day along with Lady Dixon.''

''Ah, yes, and now you and Dorothea are bosom bows, Briggs tells me.''

''Dorothea has been kind to me,'' Viola acknowledged.

''Aurora was kind to you. And so was Dorothea. Is everyone kind to you?'' he asked, annoyed and not knowing precisely why.

She lifted her head and stared him unflinchingly in the eye.

''Not everyone, my lord.''

The earl felt a stab of conscience. A totally unwarranted stab, he reminded himself. Perhaps it hadn't been kind of him to abandon her, but she had played him false, pretending to love him. He swallowed the last of his coffee.

From Brighton, Viola informed him, she went on to Averil, his country seat, accompanied by his cousin Miranda from Derbyshire.

"I wonder if you have ever given any thought to inviting her here to visit London, Richard?" she asked now. "Miranda is said to be on the shelf, but she is only two years my senior at six-and-twenty. Some gentlemen might enjoy her quiet ways."

Avery made no reply, being too occupied in searching the depths of his abominable memory, trying to recall who Miranda was. An old maid cousin, evidently. He would ask Susan, who knew every sprig on their family tree.

"She stayed with you until Christmas?" he asked.

"No. Just a month. Your cousin Yolanda would not allow any longer. I must say, Avery, that if you could speak to Yolanda about the way she bullocks Miranda it would be a kindness."

He frowned, not sure he wished to lock horns with Yolanda, whoever she was. He made a mental note to ask Susan about Yolanda, as well.

"Susan and Charles were kind enough to invite me to spend the Yuletide with them," Viola said, continuing her catalogue of the year's events. "Then I felt obliged to spend some time with my father."

"Ah, yes." Now, Mr. Challerton, Avery *did* remember. "How is your esteemed parent?"

Viola gave her head a sad shake. "Still believing that Dame Fortune will find him one day at the gaming tables, sir. I have spoken to him but he will not be sensible.''

''I suppose you want me to speak to him, as well?'' Avery asked.

''Oh, no,'' she replied quickly. ''My father is my relation, so of course I speak to him. Not that it ever does much good,'' she admitted. ''You as the head of your family can speak to Yolanda and Miranda.''

''I don't even know Miranda and Yolanda!'' he protested. ''And I'm not even sure I'd speak to either of them if I did. Has your father been hanging on your sleeve? I want the truth.''

She flushed. ''The situation is delicate, my lord. Papa cannot abstain from the cards. Add to that his predilection for drink and...''

''In the suds again?''

Her back stiffened. ''It needn't concern you.''

''No need to show hackle,'' he said dampeningly. ''It must concern me since he is my father-in-law. I'll speak to Thacker about it.'' He pushed himself away from the table.

Before he could leave, Viola gathered her courage to the sticking point.

''Avery, could I speak to you concerning Polly?''

''Don't tell me! She is yet another cousin of mine?'' he ejaculated.

Viola laughed. ''Don't be absurd. Polly is my abigail, sir.''

''Ah, yes. The one with the shrewish disposition.''

"She is not a shrew. How can you think such a thing?"

He emitted a sharp laugh. "The look in her eyes last night when I questioned her about your whereabouts."

"Polly is very loyal to me."

"She dislikes me."

"She need never come in contact with you," Viola said, feeling worried. "She is in the liveliest dread that you will turn her off. I don't believe that you would do such a thing, but if you were thinking of it, I entreat you not to do so."

"Why does she dislike me?"

Viola coloured. "I have said before she is loyal to me."

"Which means?"

She hesitated. "She felt your leaving for the Continent so soon after our wedding was an insult to me," she said at last.

"And how came she by this opinion?"

Viola's eyes widened. "It is an opinion shared by many."

"Including yourself?"

She didn't answer.

"I asked you a question, my lady. Did you share your abigail's opinion that my trip abroad was insulting to you?"

"I wasn't so much insulted, Avery, as—"

"As what?"

"Greatly saddened." She swallowed hard and looked away.

By Jove, he would not be tricked by female artifices. He had outrun them during his salad days and he would be damned if he would fall victim to them at the hands of a fortune-hunter of a wife. Avery steeled himself against taking her in his arms.

"You may do with your abigail as you wish," he said coldly.

"Thank you, Avery, and there is just other thing."

"What is it?" he asked, imperfectly masking his impatience. "I beg pardon, but I am in a bit of a rush this morning."

"You needn't tarry on my account, sir," Viola said. "Perhaps when you return we could better discuss our divorce."

Avery halted. "Our *what?*"

"Our divorce," she said, calmly staring back at him.

CHAPTER FOUR

"DID YOU SAY divorce, madam?" Avery demanded, the veins of his neck standing out vividly.

Viola's eyes widened in surprise.

"It stands to reason that you must want one," she said calmly. "Everyone knows you regretted your decision to marry me almost immediately. Why else would you bolt to the Continent and beyond?"

She paused, allowing him an opportunity to explain, and when several seconds of silence elapsed, she pressed on. "I think it best to have the word with no bark on it. I plan to make no objection to a divorce. All I ask is that it be obtained quietly."

"There has never been a bill of divorcement in my family," he said in freezing accents.

"Nor in mine," she retorted, nettled. Her lineage was every bit as respectable as his.

For most of the night she had tossed and turned, reviewing the tangled coil of her marriage until divorce suddenly flew into her mind. The more she thought of it, the more practical a scheme it became. She had saved a portion of the monthly allowance Thacker had dispensed to her throughout the year, and with some economies could live modestly on the total. Perhaps later she would seek a position as a governess or schoolmistress.

"You would willingly bear the stigma of being divorced?" Avery quizzed.

She flushed slightly, needing no reminder of Society's low view of divorce. "I have no choice, my lord."

"We could continue as we are," he pointed out, cocking his head.

Her brow cleared. "Do you plan to depart London, then, for another sojourn?" she asked.

"No, I do not," he said, annoyed at this veiled suggestion that he might prefer the road again. "Not yet, anyway. We shall discuss this later. At the moment I have a valet to win back."

A ghost of a smile passed over her face. "To be sure, my lord. I know the importance of a valet to a Corinthian such as yourself."

AVERY FLUNG his multicoloured driving cape over his shoulder as he stomped to his high-perch phaeton. Divorce. The gall of the chit.

Preposterous! One day back in London, and she was talking about a bill of divorcement. Why? Was it possible that she wished to marry another. Duvane, maybe?

Seething with anger, he drove his Welshbreds away from Berkeley Square. The team of four was usually sweet-tempered, but today they shied and fought the reins, and it was all he could do to keep them together as he headed for New Bond Street.

After two near collisions, he reached Weston's shop, where his already foul mood was rendered even more testy upon the discovery of a certain stocky red-haired gentleman being fitted for a new waistcoat.

"Richard, it is you!" Lord Newton's friendly alto boomed. "I knew you hadn't stuck your spoon in the wall. Wagered as much to John Sanders."

The earl snorted and turned to the tailor.

"I need a new rig, Weston."

"To be sure, my lord. I have just completed fitting Lord Newton and can take you next."

Newton strolled towards the floor-length mirror and turned first one way and then the other.

"What do you think, Richard?" he asked.

"I think that you should hand over my valet before I charge you with theft, Hadrian. It's bad form to steal valets from your friends. Walter is what, the fifth, you have spirited away?"

"Sixth. You forget William, who only lasted a week. He was put into a great frenzy because I could never tie a creditable *trône d'amour.*"

Weston's tape measure brought a temporary truce to the war of words between his two best customers. In no hurry to depart, Newton lingered amidst the bolts of cloth and watched Avery stand for his fitting.

After half an hour, the measurements were concluded, and Avery stepped out of the shop with his old friend at his elbow.

"Where are you bound for?" Hadrian asked, hurrying to keep up with Avery's much longer stride.

"Berry Brothers. I'm short of snuff."

"My poor fellow, what a tragedy. Have some of mine." He thrust his Sèvres snuff-box out at Avery.

Richard allowed himself a pinch.

"I rather liked the look of the blue superfine on you," Newton said, inhaling vigorously.

"Flattery won't do you any good. I still plan to take back Walter."

"Have to fight me for him," Hadrian said amiably. "He won't go willingly. I doubled his salary."

"I'll triple it."

"And he's in love with my downstairs maid."

Avery jabbed his Malacca cane at the pavement. "I wager a monkey you threw her in his path deliberately."

His friend chuckled. "You were gone a whole year, Richard. When the cat is away the mice play."

"Does that apply to wives as well as valets?" Avery murmured.

His friend snapped shut his snuff-box, the amusement vanishing from his face.

"Good Jupiter, Avery, are you accusing your wife—"

"Lud, I don't know anything to accuse her of," he complained, darting a sidelong glance at his friend. "That's why I'm asking you. You're my oldest friend, Hadrian."

"Aye, and as your oldest friend, I'll tell you to your head that it wasn't good ton to have abandoned Viola the way you did."

"I didn't abandon her," Avery protested, much stung. "I went on a trip. It just took longer than I expected."

"Why didn't you take her with you?"

Richard had known Hadrian since they were bran-faced brats at Eton, but he was loath to reveal the truth. Newton might call him a romantic for wanting love in his marriage.

"I seem to recall that you objected vociferously to my marrying Viola," Avery reminded his friend.

Newton's ruddy face turned even redder. "That was a bachelor's lament, Richard. If you stepped in parson's mousetrap, I might not be far behind. But I was wrong about Viola. She's made a hit with everyone in London, including that dragon Mrs. Drummond Burrel. Your wife is an extremely charming and beautiful young lady."

"And how do you come by that knowledge?" Avery asked, with an edge in his voice.

No slowtop, Newton took exception to his words. "By Jove, are you accusing me of dangling after your wife, Avery?" he asked, pushing back his high-crowned beaver felt. "If so you're bosky. And if you persist in such a cork-brained notion. I shall ask you to name your seconds."

"Take a damper," Avery said. "I'm not about to meet you at Paddington Green. But how do you know of Viola's charms?"

"I have eyes, gudgeon. She's invited me to several routs at your residence. Even Lady Jersey said that rarely had she enjoyed an evening more."

The earl frowned. "Who served as host to these routs?"

"Your brother-in-law, Charles Worthing, with Lady Susan's blessing. You cannot quarrel with that."

No, he couldn't, more's the pity. Often in the year past he'd imagined Viola alone and friendless in London. But she had won Hadrian's approbation. And he wasn't the only one, the earl discovered. Lady Jersey, sampling teas at the Berry Brothers emporium, bent his ear nearly in half regaling him with tales of Viola's charm and grace.

"A veritable jewel, my dear Avery," she said.

It was enough to give the earl a headache.

"A DIVORCE? Oh, no, Viola, you must be funning!" Dorothea exclaimed.

For the past fortnight, Lady Dixon had been teaching Viola the rudiments of driving a carriage in Town, but now her mind was fixed on more than the two bays pulling her barouche.

"Say you are roasting me, please!" she beseeched.

"I cannot remain married to Avery," Viola declared mulishly, trying to keep the ribbons straight as the horses rounded a corner.

"He's only been back a day," Dorothea protested.

"That's long enough," Viola said with such authority that Lady Dixon, garbed in an apricot-coloured muslin, could only wonder just what had happened between the two. Her heart went out to Viola as it had nearly a year ago when Avery had deserted her so shamefully.

But divorce! Dorothea's heart sank as she contemplated such a fate for her friend. She darted a quick look at Viola, sitting beside her in a youthful apple green frock. It was true that certain high-ranking ladies could divorce and remarry without risking the censure of Society, but it was all so dreadfully unpleasant. Would Viola be able to tolerate the on-dits sure to come her way? Of course, she acknowledged as Viola successfully turned into the Park, Viola had withstood the quizzes before. But divorce was different. And so final.

The carriage passed Stanhope Gate with the bays behaving perfectly. They shook their heads and pranced down the circular road. Since it was not the fashionable hour in the Park, the lanes were empty and Viola was able to practise her driving without distraction.

"I am getting better, am I not?" she asked Dorothea after five minutes in the Park.

Lady Dixon lifted a distracted face. "Oh, yes, my dear. So much better."

"Do you remember the first time I drove?"

Dorothea gave a convulsive shudder. "I could scarcely forget it."

"It wasn't my fault the cowman would lead his herd across the road at Green Park. It was quite silly of him, too."

"Yes. I daresay he's learned his lesson and is no longer leading his silly cows anywhere."

The two friends erupted into laughter. Dorothea was the first to recover.

"Viola, have you broached the idea of divorce to Avery?"

"Certainly, I brought it up this morning."

"And he agreed to it?"

A tiny frown puckered Viola's brows as she let the horses canter. "Actually, he was as astonished as you are. But after he has had time to consider it, I daresay it will make perfect sense to him."

"It doesn't make a particle of sense to me," Lady Dixon said. "My dear, do but consider. I know Avery's leaving you was insufferable, but now he's back. As his wife you are the Countess of Avery, with a position in Society. What will be your fate if you divorce? Unless you plan to remarry someone?"

"Heavens, no!" Viola exclaimed. Her hand tightened on the reins. She had no intention of freeing herself from one marriage only to step into another.

Viola drew the barouche to a halt near the Serpentine. From there they could watch children sail their boats across the lake. They reminded her of the family she longed for someday.

"What do you intend to do if you divorce and don't remarry?" Lady Dixon asked.

"I shall become a governess."

Dorothea's mouth opened, then shut. From countess to governess was unfathomable.

"I know what you're thinking," Viola said with a smile. "I haven't gone queer in the attic. I haven't been a countess very long, so I shan't miss it. Besides, I have known several congenial governesses, much loved by their charges. With luck I might find such a position. May I beg your assistance in the matter?"

Lady Dixon was in no way convinced that she should enlist in such an undertaking, but Viola coaxed so prettily that Dorothea at last consented.

"I know Avery's reputation as the most selfish man in London, but I still wish you would think of remaining married to him. Many marriages are difficult."

Viola shook her head emphatically. "I'm sorry, Dorothea. I'd rather risk censure from Society than continue this sham."

"Give Richard a chance. Last night at the masquerade I saw his face in passing and I believe he still cares for you."

An enigmatic look crossed Viola's face. "Believe me when I say Avery cares more about his valet than about a mere wife." She leaned over and patted her friend on the hand. "Now let us talk of more cheerful things. Like how on earth you could wear that shepherdess's costume last night. You, with your inordinate fondness for lamb cutlets!"

WHILE LADY DIXON was explaining this apparent lapse to her friend, over in the City Mr. Peter Thacker was greeting an esteemed client with enthusiasm.

"My lord, welcome back to London."

"Thank you, Thacker," Avery said, shaking hands with the thin bespectacled lawyer.

The earl glanced at Thacker's usually spotless desk now heaped high with papers.

"Good heavens, Peter, you are overworked here."

Mr. Thacker took off his gold-rimmed glasses. "On the contrary, my lord. I am not overworked; just a trifle behind."

"No doubt because of your bout with fever. Lady Avery informed me of your illness. I was sorry to hear of it."

"Thank you, my lord. Please, do sit down."

Avery accepted the invitation, stripping off his driving gloves and laying them and his Malacca cane on one corner of the lawyer's desk.

"Are you fully recovered?" he enquired. Thacker had handled his legal matters for nearly a decade, always able to decipher a clause or contract. He had drawn up the settlements for Viola's father.

"I am perfectly stout, sir, thanks in large measure to her ladyship."

"Her ladyship? Never tell me she cured you?!"

"Not exactly, sir. What I meant was that her many kindnesses helped me recover. When I fell ill the first time she sent a physician round to see me. Later she called on me daily to see how I fared."

"I'm surprised she didn't hire you a nurse," Avery murmured, wholly astonished at this benevolent image of his wife.

"Oh, she did that, too," Thacker said with a smile which came as a shock to the earl. His solicitor was usually as wooden and expressionless as they come. Avery peered more closely at the other man. Thacker appeared pale, but then so did everyone to him after his months in India.

"You say the first time you fell ill. How many times were you ill?"

"Twice, my lord."

Avery clicked his tongue. "My good fellow, you should have got out of this ghastly city air. Taken a sea cure."

Seated behind his desk, Mr. Thacker laughed. "That's what her ladyship said, my lord. She ordered me to remove myself from London. She wouldn't hear of my protesting at the cost and packed me off for a fortnight at a spa close to Brighton. She even furnished me letters of introduction to the Bishop of Bath. I protested that my clients needed my attention, but she went round to all of them and bullocked them into agreeing that I should take as much time as I required for my cure."

"Her ladyship seems to think of everything," Avery said drily.

"Oh, yes! The only thing I did not like about my illness was that she caught the infection from me."

On the verge of taking snuff from his newly filled box, Avery halted with a pinch between thumb and forefinger.

"The countess was ill?" he asked, staring at the lawyer. Rheumatic fever was dangerous. Why the devil hadn't she told him about falling sick. "When did she become ill?"

"In February, sir. She made a quick recovery. Dr. Cuthbert said her constitution was strong."

February was just two months ago. Avery stared down into his mixture of snuff. He closed the lid and put the box away. She hadn't looked unwell last night, although he couldn't really tell under all her cosmetics. He would scrutinize her more closely when he returned to Berkeley Square.

"Why wasn't I told of your illness or hers, Thacker?"

"I didn't think it proper to interject my illness into the business of handling your legal affairs. Her ladyship forbade me to mention hers. Besides, my letters were having a difficult time reaching you."

Avery shifted uncomfortably in his chair. If Viola had taken a turn for the worse, he would not have known it. But she hadn't, he reminded himself. He was making too much of the matter. She had been ill but now was well. Let it be.

"I need your assistance with a few things, Thacker," he said, coming to the point of his visit.

Mr. Thacker's Adam's apple bobbed in his throat.

"Of course, my lord. After a year's absence, you will I daresay, have many questions." He put his spectacles back on. "I have gone over the accounts from your man of business concerning the tenant farms—"

"We shall discuss the tenant farms in a moment. The first matter of concern is my roof. How badly does it leak?"

Mr. Thacker sighed. "The answer is quite badly. A rain storm nearly drenched your private rooms. Fortunately, Lady Avery had the presence of mind to remove most of your belongings. She asked me to furnish an estimate of how much the repair will cost. I have it here." He handed the document to Avery, saying, "I can engage the workmen to begin the repair straight away, sir."

"I do not desire to hear the hammering and pounding above my head," the earl replied. "When I remove to Averil for the summer, that shall be time enough for the workmen to fix the roof."

"Very good, my lord."

"The second matter I wish to discuss concerns my valet."

Mr. Thacker nodded sympathetically. "Yes, my lord, Lady Avery was most distressed that Walter chose to leave your employ."

"He didn't choose. He was stolen by Newton."

Mr. Thacker hid a smile. "Of course, my lord. Lady Avery offered to double his salary, knowing you would not like to lose Walter, but he refused."

"I want him back, Thacker."

"Lord Newton is quite taken with him."

"You are much cleverer than I in such matters. Find a way for Walter to come back."

Mr. Thacker was not certain that his duties included inducing wayward valets into returning to the fold, but he promised the earl to try to speak to Walter alone.

"Good. Now, another thing. The house on Albemarle Street. I still own the deed, do I not?"

"Of course, my lord."

Remembering the house which had served the earl's various *chères amies* over the years, Thacker was prepared for the inevitable.

"Do you wish to put it up for sale? Nothing could be easier. It has been empty for more than a year. I daresay some other gentleman could make appropriate use of it."

"You misunderstand, Thacker. I don't wish to sell it."

"Oh?" Mr. Thacker's expression turned quizzical, then thoughtful. "Then what do you wish to do with it?"

"I wish you to make certain that it is cleaned and prepared for a new occupant."

Mr. Thacker's station did not allow him to deplore the earl's muslin dealings or champion the countess's cause, legitimate though both actions might be. Still he couldn't help feeling a prick of conscience caused by the memory of Lady Avery calling on him every morning during his bout with the fever.

Perhaps the resident to be installed at Albemarle Street wasn't one of the earl's *chères amies*. And perhaps pigs could fly, too.

"You will need a butler, cook and maid for your, er, guest," he murmured, as he dipped a quill into an inkwell and wrote a list of things he must do about the house. "When will you need it ready?"

"By Tuesday, if not sooner," Avery said.

Mr. Thacker mentally counted off the days. Four days hence. Not much time. But he knew an employment service that might deliver the servants tomorrow for an interview. Meticulously, he wrote down all of the earl's staff requirements.

"I would be most obliged to you if you could meet the afternoon ferry at Dover on Tuesday and escort my guest to London for me."

"I shall be happy to meet your guest," Mr. Thacker said, though whether a high flyer would be happy to see *him* in place of the illustrious earl was another question entirely. "How shall I know her?"

"Her name is Neelah Garda. You shall have no trouble recognizing her. She will be dressed in a sari. That's a cloth which Indian women wrap about their bodies."

Mr. Thacker looked momentarily rattled. "Indian, my lord?"

"From India," the earl said. "Not from America."

"I see."

The earl lifted his lips in a rueful smile. "No, you don't see. I daresay you think me a shocking loose screw."

"Sir!"

"If anyone is entitled to that opinion it would be you, Peter. Heaven knows you draw up the settlements after my affairs have run their course. But Neelah's not my *chère amie*. She's a . . . well, it's difficult to say just what she is to me." Avery leaned back in his chair. "Have you ever heard of *suttee*, Thacker?"

"No, my lord."

The earl steepled his fingers. "It's a funeral custom in India. After a man dies, his wife commits *suttee* by throwing herself on his funeral pyre. Something about accompanying him into the afterlife."

"My word."

"Not all widows go willingly."

"I can well imagine, sir."

Avery nodded grimly. "During my travels in India I came into a village and happened upon a crowd intent on throwing the widow onto the fire. I intervened. Neelah Garda was the widow. Someone explained things to me about the custom, but by that time Neelah was clinging to me. So I felt I had no choice. I couldn't really turn her over to be killed, could I?"

"No, by heaven. What happened next, sir?"

"A great brouhaha resulted. Much shouting and even some fisticuffs. But I stood firm. Luckily Sir John Gorst was with me and led me out of the mob to safety. Neelah came with us. I felt sure that the next day, once the funeral was over Neelah could return to her own family. Her husband's family would of course have nothing to do with her, but her own relatives felt she had disgraced them by not committing suicide. She had no funds, no home any longer, and nowhere to turn. I felt responsible for her predicament. Since I was leaving India, I offered her passage to England and told her I would put her up somewhere in London. It was the least I could do until we thought of a way out of this coil.''

"Does she speak English, my lord?"

"A trifle. I have no difficulty understanding her. She is very shy and doesn't speak much."

"I daresay she was frightened. I shall be happy to escort Miss Garda from Dover."

"Good. She goes directly to Albemarle Street."

Mr. Thacker met his gaze with tacit understanding. "Yes, my lord, straight to Albemarle Street."

CHAPTER FIVE

AFTER HER DRIVING LESSON with Lady Dixon, Viola proceeded on to Hookam's, where she purchased the latest novel by Miss Austen. She had no chance to start reading it, however, because on returning home she found callers in the blue salon waiting for her.

All the racketing about she had done this morning left her fatigued, and she found herself hard pressed to follow Sir Thomas Knight's torturous recital of how he had almost captured a housebreaker running in his neighbourhood. By the end of a half hour, Lady Avery's temples were throbbing.

Then a new caller entered the room, the simian-like poet, Mr. Fortescue. At the sight of Fortescue brandishing a sheaf of poems, her other visitors rose *en masse* to make their adieus. Viola would have been convulsed in giggles if she hadn't been obliged to listen to Mr. Fortescue read one ode after another.

Viola sat through the recital with aching temples. To distract herself, she concentrated on images of the sea at Brighton. Perhaps she could go again this year. She frowned. Would Avery want to go to Brighton? Could she go without him? How vexatious! When he was absent she would not scruple to pick up and leave, but could she do so while he was still in London. Clearly, having a husband installed under the same roof made life infinitely more complicated.

"How was that, my lady?"

Mr. Fortescue's query brought her out of her brown study.

"Oh, first-rate, sir."

The poet beamed. "Which part did you enjoy the most?"

"The ending," she said truthfully. "And now, your throat must be parched after all your reading. Won't you take some sherry?"

Mr. Fortescue condescended to accept a glass of sherry, but no more than a sip had he taken before he found himself scrutinized by a pair of lazy blue eyes he remembered only too well.

"My lord."

Viola, who had been wondering what to do with Mr. Fortescue, seized upon Avery's presence with an excess of enthusiasm.

"Oh, Mr. Fortescue, pray forgive me. Here is Avery, whom I promised to accompany on a promenade round the square. I quite forgot the time, my dear. I shall be ready in a trice, and thank you so much for reading me your delightful verse, Mr. Fortescue."

"Any time, dear lady. Permit me to say that you are my inspiration." The poet clasped her hand and bestowed a damp salute upon it before bowing to Avery and leaving.

Avery advanced into the room, swinging his quizzing glass.

"Doing it much too brown, my dear. My memory may be shockingly bad, but I would have certainly remembered a rendezvous to promenade with you anywhere."

"I know it was wrong to dissemble," she said without a blink, "but I had to say something or I would be obliged to listen to his tedious verse for another hour. And I could not. I already have the headache."

"Temples throbbing?" he asked sympathetically.

"Yes."

Before she could utter another word he grasped her head between his palms.

"What are you doing!" she cried, trying to pull away from the unexpected touch of his bare fingertips on her skin.

"Don't be missish," he commanded. "I'm your husband."

"But what are you doing?" She continued to squirm.

"Be still and you will see." He began rubbing her temples in a circular motion with his thumbs. The light, warm movement was surprisingly soothing. "It's a massage technique I learned when I was in Asia."

"From the Indians?" she asked, disconcerted by the steady rhythm and the coolness of his fingertips.

"No, it was a Chinese chap on board ship," Avery said. "A doctor from Shanghai. He knew a good deal about herbs and spoke at great length about the *yin* and the *yang* of the body and the importance of balancing the interior.''

''My interior needs no balancing,'' she protested.

He smiled down at her. ''That's not what the Chinese chap would say. He showed me different areas of the body to press on. If your tooth aches, you press here.'' He picked up her hand and pointed to the web of flesh between her thumb and forefinger.

''That's absurd. It's nowhere near a tooth.''

''Yes, I know. But one fellow on the boat who had a toothache said it worked.'' He went back to rubbing her temples, slowly and smoothly. ''How does your head feel now?''

''Much better,'' she said truthfully. ''Thank you.''

''I trust you spent a congenial morning before the poet arrived,'' he asked, dropping his hands to his side.

''Dorothea took me for a drive. She is teaching me the rudiments of Town driving.''

He looked up in quick alarm. ''Good Jupiter! Are you mad? Dixon's carriages are always in repair because she turns over a vehicle every month.''

''You have been away a year. In that time she hasn't turned over a vehicle even once.''

''Remind me to congratulate her on so notable a feat,'' he said drily. ''We must go for a drive soon, just the two of us, so I may discern your progress.''

Nothing filled Viola with more trepidation than the thought of holding the reins with a member of the Four Horse Club on the seat next to her.

''I am a mere whipster, sir.''

"You must have learned something or else your teacher is at fault. I dimly recall your asking me to teach you once."

She coloured slightly. That was when they were courting. He had said yes.

"Yes, I know, my lord. But you were not in London."

"I am now. I could take over the lessons." He glanced at her, watching the flickering emotions on her face.

Resolutely, Viola shook her head. "I know you are a top sawyer, sir. But I don't think I should change horses—that is to say, teachers—in midstream, should I?"

"Very true." Avery was conscious of a twinge of disappointment. It would have been amusing to teach her the rudiments of driving a carriage in Town, to see that lovely face light up with excitement.

"How were your errands?" Viola asked now. "I trust you filled your snuff-box."

"To the brim," he said, taking it out and flicking it open with one hand. "You don't take snuff, ma'am, do you?"

"Good gracious, Avery, what a thought!"

He inhaled a pinch. "I didn't mean to give offence, but as you are so fond of telling me, I have been away a year, and you could have picked up odd habits during my absence."

"Not that odd, my lord."

He snapped his box shut. "I also ran into Lady Jersey at the Berry Brothers. She spoke highly of you as being a rare jewel. I didn't know you were at first oars with her."

"She's been very kind to me."

"Ah, one of those." His blue eyes glinted.

"It's the truth," she said sharply.

"I believe you, though I wish she didn't talk so much. When I left her *I* had the headache."

"Perhaps I should massage your temples, sir."

These words were lightly spoken, but he looked at her so meaningfully that she nearly bit her tongue.

"You found Mr. Thacker well, I hope?" she asked quickly to hide her confusion.

"Very well." The earl frowned, remembering what Thacker had said about her illness. "He also told me that you went to his home during his most recent illness. In the future I forbid it. It's for your own protection," he went on. "Thacker told me you fell ill. Those visits to his residence undoubtedly had something to do with it."

"Visiting the sick is a Christian duty. I often accompanied my aunt," Viola declared, chafing under the high-handed orders he was issuing.

"This is not Gloucestershire, madam," he said witheringly. "Do you wish to be carried off with the next epidemic that sweeps London?"

"You exaggerate."

He shook his head. "I've seen illness in the palaces I've visited. Heed me on this matter. You may send food, a nourishing broth, gruel to the sick, but do not place your person under their roofs. I'd wager a pony that's how you fell ill to rheumatic fever. Why the devil did you omit that fact when you were cataloguing your year for me this morning?"

"There was no necessity."

"I shall be the judge of that, and I will have the particulars now, if you please."

"It doesn't please me," she retorted, then spread her hands out helplessly. "Really, Avery, there is nothing I dislike more than being ill unless it is talking about the illness. My Aunt Simmons was prone to quack herself, and I vowed that I would never follow suit."

This was a side to the Simmons household he did not know. Viola rarely spoke about her aunt.

"How many days were you sick with the rheumatic fever?" he asked.

"Just a few."

"Does that mean one or two?" he asked skeptically.

"Five," she admitted. "But the fever broke by the fourth day. And that is all I wish to say about it."

She did not wish to recall those feverish days when she was out of her head and crying his name in her delirium. She had sworn her servants to secrecy on that matter already.

"I know our marriage has been a trifle unusual," he said in a gentler tone. "But you *are* my wife, and I wish to be informed when you feel unwell in the future."

She moved away from him, not liking the feelings that his concern stirred within her. She was a widgeon to be nursing a tendre for a man who had abandoned her so publicly.

"Be careful what you wish, my lord," she said, trying for a lighter tone. "I could break out in a rash or start coughing at the most inopportune moment, perhaps when you are sitting down to a winning hand at Brook's or White's. How tedious it will be for you to tear yourself away from the green baize tables."

"I'll risk it," he said, unable to resist a chuckle.

"Why did you come back, Avery?" she asked, before she could stop herself.

He glanced up sharply. He had asked that question of himself as well.

He gazed into her eyes. *Fortune-hunter,* he reminded himself, lest he become lost in that violet sea. "Because I was tired of travelling. What other reason could there be?" he asked sardonically.

Viola looked away, blinking hard. So the absentee earl was tired of travelling. That was the only reason he had returned.

"Have you given any further thought to our divorce?" she asked.

He flicked open his snuff-box again and dipped two fingers in. "No. I'm afraid I had no occasion to ponder the matter. It's a pity you don't take snuff, because I could do with another opinion. I think this mixture is too dry."

"Perhaps you will ponder it now."

He inhaled another pinch. "Definitely too dry."

"Avery, do stop bamming me. Our divorce is a serious matter which needs our attention."

"Does it need our attention now, this very minute?" he asked plaintively.

"I find that I must use my time with you expediently," she said, "lest you suddenly depart on another trip."

"I can allay your fears on that point, madam. I have planned no trip in the immediate future."

"Did you plan your last trip?" she asked.

Her question surprised him. "No, that one was quite impromptu."

Impromptu, was it, Viola fumed. He had fled from the very idea of marriage to her. She wouldn't give him the satisfaction of crying. She blinked back her tears.

"About our divorce, my lord—" she pressed on.

"Will you stop this prattle about divorce," he ordered, snapping his snuff-box shut and nearly catching his thumb-nail. "I find the topic disagreeable."

"So do I. But as we are both agreed that our marriage is undesirable, the simplest thing would be to begin the proceedings to end it."

"Simplest thing?" Avery shook his head. "It is by no stretch of the imagination a simple task to undo a marriage, my dear. That's why some bachelors are understandably reluctant to step into parson's mousetrap."

"As I recall, my lord, no one forced you to make an offer for me."

Only his foolish heart. "For us to divorce would require an act of Parliament," he said now. "Something inordinately difficult to arrange. Just look at the problems Prinny has had. Even a quiet bill of divorcement such as you envisage would be heard in public and scrutinized. You won't be able to imagine the scandal. Do you wish to have your good name bandied about?"

"I am quite accustomed to it," she shot back coolly, "since my name has been bandied about for months after your abrupt departure on the day of our wedding."

"This would be different."

She laughed. "Yes, it would. *Your* name would be bandied about by all. *You* would be forced to endure the taunts and ill-timed remarks of the Bond Street beaux."

"Is marriage to me such a hardship?" he asked, annoyed by the tone of the conversation. First she had used all her wiles to marry him and now she wanted to be rid of him. "Do you not enjoy rank and position? Have I forced myself upon you, as other husbands do their wives?"

"Yes, yes, and we both know the answer to the third is no," she said sharply.

"There has been no divorce in the family," he said coldly. "If you pursue the matter, you will find it difficult. And if you succeed you shall get not a groat from me."

Viola glared at him. Of all the insufferable remarks. She didn't want his money. Not a penny of it.

"And now I'd as lief eat as talk about divorce."

"Very well, my lord. Enjoy your nuncheon." She turned towards the door.

He frowned. "Aren't you in the habit of taking a noon meal?" he asked.

"Ordinarily yes, but I find myself with little appetite."

"Perhaps I should summon a doctor and have you examined for consumption," he said irritably. "You barely ate a morsel at breakfast. You will collapse without nourishment."

"If you, my husband, order me to eat I suppose I dare not refuse."

He threw his hands up in exasperation. "Eat or do not eat. It's all the same to me. In point of fact, I find my own appetite dwindling quickly. I shall take my meal elsewhere and leave you to your fasting alone."

ODIOUS, ODIOUS MAN. Viola read and re-read the lines of print on the opening page of Miss Austen's latest work. It was hopeless. All she saw when she stared down at the page was Avery's infuriating countenance.

He didn't wish a discussion of their divorce, so there would be no discussion. *He* didn't approve of her visits to the sick, so she would not visit the sick. *He* wished her to eat, so she must eat. These high-handed methods made it clear that to remain married to Avery would constitute a penance of the highest order.

And what of his warning that she would not get a groat from him if they divorced! She hurled the book down on the prized Wilton, where it bounced before settling against the Egyptian couch. As though all she wanted from him was his purse.

She picked up a fringe she had been knotting earlier in the week, and her fingers worked the yarn, finding relief for her fury. By the end of twenty minutes, her mind was calm. Flying into the boughs was not the way out of this muddle. Sensibly, she reviewed her previous plan to become a governess. She was more determined than ever to press forward with that scheme. It might be difficult to be at someone's beck and call but probably not more difficult than what she had previously experienced in her aunt's household. Tongues would wag, but she had borne the unkind remarks of strangers before.

While she was composing a mental list of those families who might need a governess, Lady Susan was announced.

"I came to see Richard," Lady Susan declared, sweeping into the blue room. "But Briggs informed me he was out. Dare I hope he returns before another year passes, my dear?"

Her good-humoured jest failed to elicit even a ghost of a smile from Viola.

"He wished to seek a noon meal elsewhere."

"How peculiar of him," said Lady Susan, eyeing Viola speculatively. "Henri is quite the equal of any chef in London."

She leaned down and picked up Viola's discarded book.

"Has that brother of mine explained his absence to you yet?" Susan asked, turning the pages idly.

"Explain?" Viola hooted. "Avery is my husband and as such not obliged to explain anything to a mere wife."

"Did he say that?" Susan replied. "Heavens, he *has* lost his wits, probably because of the scorching sun in the East. We must put our minds together and find a way of curing him of this or his idiocy shall know no limits."

Viola could not help laughing at that. How she yearned to confide in Susan about a divorce, but she knew instinctively that her sister-in-law would try to dissuade her from this course of action. Avery's family was Susan's family, too. Any hint of scandal would touch her, as well.

"I really don't care why he left or why he has returned," Viola said now.

Lady Susan did not press the issue, settling more comfortably on the couch and turning to the more agreeable topic of the burglars still at large in London.

"There's been another break-in. This time on Mount Street," she said. "Sir Frederick Harding's residence. The thieves got away with Lady Anne's best jewels.

The peculiar thing is that there was no sign of forced entry."

"That means they had a key, perhaps, or climbed through an open window," Viola said. "It's a pity that Sir Frederick didn't prepare a plan."

"Oh, Frederick always was a coxcomb." Lady Susan offered her opinion freely. "The only one who could abide him was Duvane. I always thought Anne was foolish to marry Frederick, but she wouldn't take after three Seasons and finally agreed to the match. That was two years and two babies ago."

"Do they have a governess?" Viola asked, bending down and retrieving the forgotten fringe.

"I don't know. A nurse, I'm sure. Why?"

"No reason." Viola silently added the Hardings to her list of possible employers. "Do go on about Sir Frederick." It would behoove her to know more about the baronet in case he was to hire her.

"He's a boastful sort of man, inclined to think that he knows best."

"A trait common to males," Viola said, thinking of one male in particular.

"There's talk now of offering a reward for the capture of the culprits. All the victims have agreed to contribute a hundred pounds each. The total would amount to twelve hundred pounds."

"Twelve hundred pounds!" Viola exclaimed, pushing away the fringe.

Lady Susan dimpled with amusement. "Are you short of pin money, my dear?"

Twelve hundred pounds would enable Viola to live comfortably by herself after her divorce. "I'm tempted to find the housebreakers myself and claim the reward," Viola admitted.

"But it could be dangerous. Besides, Avery will surely not approve."

"Probably not!" Viola agreed. But the thought only had the result of making her more determined than ever to capture the burglars and claim the reward for herself.

She said no more on the subject, and Lady Susan hoped that she had convinced her sister-in-law to give up any idea of bringing the criminals to justice.

"I am so looking forward to hearing you play tonight at the Fogarty musicale," she said to Viola, turning to another matter on her mind.

"I'm not certain I shall be attending."

Susan's eyes widened. "What is this? Lady Fogarty told me that you had consented to play your flute."

"I haven't yet told Avery about it. Do you think he will want to attend after his long trip back?"

"If I know my brother, I think it is not the fatigue which will cause him to decline but the musicale itself. The last time Richard went to a musicale was five years ago, and he complained the harp-playing sounded like just so much stupid plucking. But even if he doesn't go that shouldn't stop you. Charles and I shall be happy to be your escorts."

"He may forbid me to attend," Viola said, looking dark.

"Fustian! Why would he do such a thing?"

"Because he is the most odious, high-handed man in the kingdom," Viola said, venting her spleen at last.

Lady Susan was well acquainted with her brother's flaws, but even she blinked at this scorching recital.

"What has he done to you?" she asked anxiously, her mind flying at once to the possibility that in asserting his husbandly rights Richard had shocked an innocent like Viola.

"Nothing, except to remind me that under his roof I am a veritable nobody. That whatever he says takes precedent over my wishes. If I wish to attend the musicale and he wishes me to sit by the fire, I am to sit by the fire."

"He cannot have been so unfeeling."

"Oh, yes, he can."

"Richard always was prone to freakish whims. Many husbands are at first. But there is a knack to handling them, my dear." She leaned forward with a conspiratorial wink.

Viola laughed. "Don't tell me you are going to give me advice on how to handle Avery, Susan. I vow that is what my Aunt Simmons tried to do on my wedding day."

"It's more on how to conduct yourself." Lady Susan said with a wise smile. "You can rant and rave and storm and cry and the gentlemen will be unmoved. But if you toss your head and laugh they will pay attention. Just don't take what he says too much to heart.

A gay countenance, a trill of laughter. Do you remember what I told you last year?''

Indeed, Viola did remember. It was Lady Susan who had schooled her on how to keep a happy pose in public. But much as she wanted to follow her advice now, she couldn't. How could she keep from taking what Avery said to heart when her heart itself was nearly broken because of him?

CHAPTER SIX

"RICHARD, I must have a word with you."

Lady Susan's unexpected greeting, punctuated with a sharp poke of her finger into the back of Avery's neck, caught the earl just as he opened his mouth to a forkful of Clarendon's famous steak-and-kidney pie. Instinctively, he inhaled. The chunk of beef became lodged at once in his windpipe. He spluttered, changing his face to such a vivid purple that Lady Susan began pounding him vigorously on the back to dislodge the meat.

"Susan, why must you resort to fisticuffs every time we meet?" he gasped finally when he could speak.

"What a coming thing to say when I practically saved your life just now," she said, dropping into a chair at his table. "I vow, if I were a more vapourish female I would have swooned. I was in the liveliest dread that you would choke to death. A very nasty scene that would be. I recollect Totlinger's eldest son died from eating a peach. You know what a greedy creature he was. He ate it too fast and choked to death on the pit."

"What amusing anecdotes you do dredge up from that indefatigable memory of yours," her brother complained, taking a sip of water and then wiping his mouth meticulously with a napkin.

"Do you remember as a child how Nanny always used to strike your knuckles for bolting your food as though you were starving?" Susan quizzed.

"No," came the acid rejoinder. "I have taken great pains to forget it. I warn you I am not in the mood to trade childhood reminiscences, particularly about Nanny who terrorized us so. How did you find me, anyway?" he went on, as she picked up a fork and sampled a portion of his meat pie.

"I stopped by at Berkeley Square and learned you were dining out. I remembered Clarendon's was your favourite restaurant."

"You should have been a detective. What's afoot?"

Lady Susan also wiped her mouth with a napkin. "I daresay you will tell me it is none of my concern, but Viola seemed quite unhappy. Your abandonment of her was very wrong, Richard. What possessed you to do such a thing?"

Avery stiffened and picked up his wineglass. "You were right, dear sister. This is none of your affair," he spoke with a trace of hauteur.

Lady Susan waved a dismissive hand. "It certainly is mine when I am left to comfort a distraught bride who can neither eat nor talk for weeks. It's my affair when gossip columns are filled with speculation about my brother's odd behaviour."

"Gossip columns?"

She emitted a sigh. "Don't be a nodcock, Richard. Your absence was the chief on-dit of the past Season. You can imagine what the bow-window set had to say about you and Viola."

"Odd, no one has said a thing to me."

"Oh, they wouldn't dare say it to your face. They are not stupid. It's safer to roast someone in print when he is out of Town than in."

"Viola was in Town."

"Viola does not have the authority you command, gudgeon. One of your set-downs is not worth the price they pay."

"Really? I had no inkling." He applied himself once more to his plate. "I suspect that you have exaggerated the trials of my wife. She seems much recovered from being the target of the quizzes. With your help, I daresay?" he said, hazarding a guess.

Lady Susan rearranged the sleeve of her gown, which was perilously close to dipping into the sauce from the meat pie.

"You cannot quarrel with my helping Viola. It kept me amused and it kept her out the briars."

"I do not consider having *cicisbeos* like Duvane dangling after my wife to be keeping her out of the briars."

Far from being offended, Lady Susan was delighted by this sign of proprietary interest in Viola.

"Richard, I do believe you are jealous."

The earl snorted. "Just because I don't want to see loose fish dangling after Viola—"

"There is nothing wrong with a married lady having admirers," Lady Susan replied placidly. "Indeed, many husbands encourage the practice because it frees them to pursue their other tiresome interests like cards and sport."

"I do not see any *cicisbeo* dangling after you," he pointed out.

Lady Susan nodded, acknowledging this hit. "That's because Charles discourages them from doing so."

"My point exactly."

"Do you plan another trip soon?" she asked, abruptly changing the subject.

"No," he said, rather put out at these overt attempts to have him travelling again. "I've just come back. I own to considerable exhaustion."

"You don't look at all exhausted," she said, studying him closely. "Though you are very brown. I would be failing in my duties as your sister if I didn't tell you to trim your hair. I am glad you are staying in England. Viola might not survive a second departure."

"You credit her with more sensibility than she possesses. She is not such a ticklish creature, I assure you."

"How do you know that?" she asked.

The earl hunched a shoulder. "I do, that's all."

The sheer stupidity of this remark snapped Lady Susan's control.

"You only courted her for two weeks and then left her. How would you know anything at all about this wife of yours?" she demanded.

"I know all I need know about her," her brother muttered. Including the most important; the chit was a fortune-hunter.

"Richard, you must put aside whatever quarrel you had with Viola and start acting in a responsible way towards her."

Avery tossed his napkin down on the table. "Responsible? I have paid her father's debts, given her rank and position beyond her dreams. All the time I was away I left instructions for my lawyer to give her whatever monies she needed. Is that what you call irresponsibility, madam?"

"No."

"You may rest assured I do not plan another trip for now. I plan to stay under my roof, leaking though it is, and live as I wish. I trust you have no quarrel with that?"

"Of course not."

"By the by, if you have any influence on Viola, you might attempt to dissuade her from divorce. She has got that maggot in her brain somehow."

"Divorce!" Lady Susan exclaimed, then looked over her shoulders anxiously for fear of being overheard. "You can't mean it, Richard. It would be too much for poor Viola to bear."

Avery ran a finger between his neck and collar points. "Do stop calling her poor Viola. It's not my doing. It's hers. She continues to bring up the disagreeable topic of divorce to me whenever we have two minutes alone with each other. My wife does not wish to remain married to me.''

"Who could fault her?" Susan said at once. "You've behaved quite odiously towards her. You must coax her out of this notion.''

"I'd sooner coax an ox.''

"Have you even attempted to display a tenth part of that charm you are so famous for, Avery? I hate to enlarge your consequence, but even Lady Paver who has sixty years in her dish told me that she felt her heart skip a beat one evening when you shook hands with her. If you would only try to be civil to Viola I know she would fall top over tail in love with you—''

"A husband does not need love from his wife, Susan,'' Avery said in a voice so daunting that Lady Susan fell silent.

He rose from the table, unwilling to tolerate any more talk of Viola. Nor did he want to think about charming her, or her falling in love with him. He had deluded himself on that head once before. He would not make that mistake again.

"DRAT AND BOTHERATION!"

Viola stood in front of the library door, frozen like one of Mr. Gunter's ice carvings. She had thought it best to ask Avery's permission—detestable word!—to attend Lady Fogarty's musicale, but hearing him roar within his book room did not augur well for her request.

As she stood pensively eyeing the solid oak door, Briggs approached, carrying a tray of restoratives.

"Is he in a *very* foul temper, Briggs?" she asked.

"No, my lady. Not so very foul. Just in a bit of a pucker because he hasn't been able to persuade Walter to return. Every letter he writes to Walter is returned by Lord Newton's footman. If you give him twenty minutes with this prime Madeira, he will be feeling more the thing, my lady," the butler said.

"Thank you, Briggs. An excellent suggestion."

Twenty minutes later, when at last she entered the library, Viola found Avery in a curricle chair by the fire with a copy of *Gentleman's Quarterly*, a veritable pattern-card of amiability itself.

"Avery, I promised Lady Fogarty that I would play my flute at her musicale this evening. May I please keep my promise to her?" Viola asked, taking her fences in a rush. The only way she was able to utter the word "please" without choking was to say it quickly.

The earl lowered his magazine.

"I didn't know you played the flute. Don't tell me—" he held up a hand "—it is an instrument you have just learned to play this year." His smile took the sting from his words.

She flashed a smile back and took the chair opposite his.

"Actually, I have always played it. What say you, sir? About my going to the musicale tonight?"

He stretched a hessian out to the fire.

"I think it a splendid notion. I look forward to hearing my wife play."

"Oh, you needn't come yourself!" she said, alarmed at the idea of him in the audience.

He glanced up sharply.

"I know you prefer the pleasures of White's and Brook's. Susan tells me that you cannot abide musicales. You mustn't feel obliged to suffer simply on my behalf."

"It is no obligation. I shall be happy to attend."

Now why in thunderation did I say that, Avery wondered, after Viola had left the library. He turned a page of his magazine, an old issue he had been perusing. Susan was right. He loathed musicales. If Viola wished to attend and play her flute, let her. There was no necessity for him to make an appearance.

And yet he wanted to.

He turned another page of the magazine, laughing out loud at the gossip columns until he came to a sketch near the bottom. His face hardened when he saw a caricature which could only be of himself.

He was not mentioned by name, but who else could be dubbed the Absentee Earl? In the sketch, the absentee earl was lounging on a gondola on a Venetian canal while his wife, whose face bore a striking resemblance to a viola, cried her eyes out in a London Town house.

Avery tore the page from the magazine and crushed it in his fist. Then he hurled it into the fire. It was unconscionable to mock him so. He would cancel his subscription to the magazine.

Another thought struck him as he watched the flames consume the hated sketch: had Viola seen it?

This must have been what Susan had meant when she told him about the scorn heaped up on him during his absence. How many of his friends had seen this issue and laughed themselves silly at his expense? And Viola's. For a moment something akin to regret tugged at the earl's heart-strings.

By Jove, he had not meant to subject Viola to such insults. He had been very angry at being duped into marriage, but he did not intend her to be subject to such mortification.

Or had he?

Conscience-stricken, he pushed the Madeira away. He would go to the dratted musicale and dance attendance on his wife. That would put an end to whatever the quizzes were saying. Feeling much better, he went off to instruct James on the importance of starch in a gentleman's neckcloth.

"WHAT PIECE DO YOU INTEND to play tonight?" Avery asked as they rode in his Town carriage to the Fogarty musicale. He smiled at Viola, seated next to him in her creamy muslin gown. "Bach, perhaps?"

"Nothing so grand," she assured him. "It is my own composition."

"Indeed? What do you call it?"

She hesitated. The piece she had called in private "The Traveller" but she dared not mentioned such a title to his face.

"It is as yet untitled."

"Oh, but we must find a name for it."

They were still exchanging possible titles for her composition when they entered the Fogarty establishment. Standing on the marble stairs shaking hands with her guests, Lady Fogarty cast a stricken look at the earl and shrank back into the arms of her spouse. Fogarty, far from being appreciative of her sensibility, thrust her away.

"Now, Avery, you won't throw a despicable scene, I implore you," Lady Fogarty said. "Everyone knows how you detest musicales."

Avery's lips twitched in amusement.

"I am here only to enjoy Viola's playing."

"Good." Lady Fogarty peered towards his right. "Ah, yes, Viola. The very one I must talk to. I must have a word in private with you about the program tonight."

So saying, she momentarily abandoned Fogarty in the receiving line and bustled Viola off to a small corner of the room.

"What about the program, ma'am?" Viola prodded gently.

Lady Fogarty inhaled a majestic breath and thumped her bosom. "Lady Harding was supposed to have led off tonight's series, but since falling victim to housebreakers, she finds her nerves so unsettled she cannot play a note."

"I can well imagine. Is she here tonight?" Viola asked, hoping she could question Lady Harding herself about the robbery. If she were to claim the reward for the capture of the burglars, she would need to know every particle of information she could find.

"No, she is too busy quacking herself. I myself do not see how quacking oneself is of the slightest use *after* one has lost one's best jewels to the burglars. Will you play first, Viola?"

"Certainly."

After Lady Fogarty resumed her place next to her lord, Viola took a turn in the drawing room. Avery stood deep in conversation with Lord Dixon while Dorothea, off to one side, admired a huge arrangement of roses. Immediately Viola made her way to her friend and enquired about any openings for governesses.

"Oh, don't ask me that, Viola," Lady Dixon implored. "I'd hoped you would forget all about that wretched idea."

"Do you mean that you haven't made the slightest effort to enquire for me? Dorothea, I am quite in earnest about pursuing a life as a governess."

"My dear, you have no idea of the hardships of their life," Lady Dixon said, sniffing a particularly fragrant yellow rose in the vase in front of them. "If you would just talk to one, you would abandon this idiotish notion."

"What a splendid idea! But how shall I meet a governess and ask her about her life?"

"You can't." Dorothea uttered a despairing sigh. "Just think of the gossip if the Countess of Avery were to make enquiries into the life of a governess? How peculiar that would seem."

"What a pity all your children are grown and you do not have a governess any more," Viola said.

"Yes, we pensioned her off. But I do recollect how fond she was of a certain tea room, called the Rose Garden, in Piccadilly. If you went there you might find a governess to speak to who would surely dissuade you from this rackety idea."

"That is the perfect notion!" Viola exclaimed. The governesses might know what other families needed help. Her mind teemed with plans. If she wore her oldest dress and bonnet, no one would know her as the Countess Avery.

She was still contemplating what dress she would wear when Lady Fogarty signalled them into the music room.

"Ready?" Avery asked. Viola started. He mistook that for a sign of nerves and squeezed her hand in reassurance, which she found even more disconcerting. They followed the crowd into the music room and Avery led her to the front row. She sat with the flute clasped tightly in her hands.

Lady Fogarty welcomed her guests, then announced that Lady Avery would be leading off the program with a special composition on her flute.

A brief round of applause greeted this news.

"At least it's not a harp," Lord Fabersham muttered.

Avery swivelled his head and glared at Fabersham, then turned back to watch Viola. She looked angelic in her white muslin, which as fashion dictated was as gauzy as possible. She lifted the flute to her lips...the same soft lips he had pressed against his last night.

The first notes sounded, and Avery forgot all about Viola's lips. The melody she played was so plaintive, so evocative, that he felt the notes in the deepest recesses of his heart. The haunting music sent a chill down his spine. It spoke of longing and love. He could not help but be moved. The chit truly had a gift.

Avery was not the only one mesmerized by the music coming from the silver flute. Lady Fabersham, two rows behind, burst into tears and was followed by her husband, who had a sentimental disposition.

Engrossed in her performance, Viola did not notice. When she was in the thrall of her music, she thought of nothing else. She remembered exactly when she had written the piece. It was two weeks after her wedding, when she had been feeling lonely and abandoned, unloved and scorned. She looked up as the last note hung in the air, and met Avery's eyes.

Then quickly she looked away.

The room was hushed, then applause swept through the audience like a tidal wave, nearly bringing down the chandeliers swaying over Viola's head. She flushed with pleasure.

"Bravo," Avery whispered as she sank back into the chair next to his.

A warm glow of satisfaction suffused her whole body. Her heart was full. Avery's blue eyes were proud, proud of *her*. She continued to think of his whispered bravo as Miss Taylor stumbled through a Haydn sonata on the pianoforte and Miss Blaine followed with a ponderous rendition of one of Mozart's more sprightly tunes.

Viola's composition was acclaimed as the hit of the evening.

"When did you write it?" Avery asked in the refreshment room as he put two lobster patties on her plate.

"Some time ago," Viola confessed. When she was beginning to fear he would never return.

He speared a sweetmeat for each of them.

"Whom did you write it for?" he enquired.

Viola was taken aback by this question. Had the pain of her abandonment been so evident in the music? She had been furious when she wrote it. How could she answer truthfully and not spark another quarrel? She didn't wish to constantly be at daggers drawn with him.

"No one in particular, my lord," she said now.

Avery had noticed that momentary hesitation before she answered. Like most honest people, Viola did not have the talent for dissembling. She had written the piece for someone. When Duvane sidled up and she turned with enthusiasm to greet him, Avery was certain he knew exactly what gentleman had inspired his wife.

Stung by the fact that his wife would compose such a musical triumph for a card cheat like Duvane, he returned a barely civil greeting to the viscount.

"Do you find many changes in London since your year away, Avery?" Duvane asked the earl.

"I find some things unchanged—like you," Avery replied with a wintry smile.

Viola lifted a brow. She knew Avery's dislike of Duvane. Tonight that was particularly vexing because she did so want to ask Duvane about Lady Harding's burglary. The viscount lived just a short distance from where the break-in had taken place. But she couldn't quiz him with the earl present.

"Richard, the lobster has made me thirsty," she said, a ploy which caused the viscount to volunteer his services.

"I shall be glad to fetch a glass of champagne to soothe your parched lips," Duvane said.

"I shall soothe my wife's parched lips, damn your impudence," Avery said, his chin jutting out challengingly.

"Avery, please. All I want is something to drink."

The earl stalked off to the refreshment table. Viola seized her opportunity to ask Duvane about the Harding burglary.

"Is it true about the reward?"

"Yes," Duvane disclosed. "Harding wants to recover the necklace. But these criminals are too clever by half. They came in while the Hardings were out walking in the Park, ransacked their rooms and stole the jewels.''

"But weren't the jewels in a safe place?"

Duvane shrugged. "Of course, but the thieves found it. They took a diamond necklace, a ruby brooch and a signet ring.''

"The ring would be worthless to anyone but Harding.''

The viscount nodded his agreement. "Unless the thieves sell it to someone who can recut the stone.''

"How horrid. It makes me glad that I have no jewels.''

"You have that lovely wedding ring," he said, taking her hand and holding the ring up to the light. "I see you are wearing it tonight, while you were not last night.''

"I'd be obliged to you, Duvane, if you would take your hands off my wife's.'' Only a fool glancing at the cold fury in the earl's blue eyes would think he wasn't serious. Duvane dropped Viola's hand.

"Here is your champagne, my dear," Avery said.

"Thank you, Richard.''

She took a sip. Duvane bowed and left them.

"You're not drinking very much," Avery said after ten minutes, when her glass was still nearly full. "Perhaps you did not really want the champagne, after all?'' Perhaps it was just a ruse to allow her to have a word with the man she loved.

"I find it gives me the headache," she said truthfully, then wondered if he would offer her that Chinese massage again. But he merely shrugged and said since she was unwell they leave.

The carriage ride home seemed endless. Avery watched Viola's every move. The moonlight falling through the window spilled across her slender hands, the same hands Duvane had held.

Avery could see the even rise and fall of her breasts under the gauzy muslin. Damn it. She was lovely and his wife, but much good that did him. She was charmed by this coxcomb Duvane. It was plain as two pins that Viola wrote that composition for Duvane. She had certainly greeted him enthusiastically and dispatched her husband on a bogus errand to be alone with him.

The carriage stopped. Avery escorted her to the door, then turned back towards the street.

"You are not coming in?" she asked.

"I find that you were right when you spoke this afternoon about the pleasures to be found at White's and Brook's. I am eager to try my luck."

She stifled her feeling of disappointment. "I wish you a good night, then, my lord."

"Good night."

CHAPTER SEVEN

"AVERY HAS the devil's own luck," Lord Peter Sykes complained good-naturedly as he tossed his cards down in the card-room at White's.

The circle of heads round the green baize table bobbed their agreement with Lord Peter as the earl won yet another hand.

"At least it's Richard who's winning and not Duvane," the young Marquis of Valie pointed out.

"I didn't know Duvane sat down to cards at White's," the earl said, frowning slightly.

"Every night, as a rule." Sykes dabbed his forehead with a lace handkerchief. "An hour ago I saw him look in here, but he was disinclined to take a chair."

Little wonder, Avery thought. Duvane was not foolish enough to cheat at his table.

During the next hour the number of players dwindled until at last only Avery and Sykes remained in the room.

"I think we have had enough, Peter, don't you?" Avery asked, reaching for his coat.

"I certainly have *lost* enough," Sykes said with a grimace. "I can't pay you the full sum."

"Why don't we just cancel the debt," Avery said kindly. He knew Sykes was purse-pinched and had no desire to reduce him to penury.

But his suggestion wounded young Sykes. "Avery! I can't do that. My honour as a gentleman is at stake. I'd pay you today in full if it weren't for the wretched trust my father set up. My uncle keeps me on a very short string," he complained. "I need time to come up with the ready. Truth is, I owe a considerable sum to Duvane, as well. I've never seen a fellow with his luck. Every time he sits down to play he wins."

"And what do you deduce from that?" Avery raised his brows at the other fellow.

Although in his cups, Sykes immediately grasped the meaning of Avery's words.

"Are you suggesting he's a Captain Sharp?"

"If a man will win every time you sit down with him, perhaps you should seek the company of others."

Lord Peter nodded. "Perhaps I should. Obliged to you, Avery. My allowance comes next month. I promise to pay you every farthing I owe."

"Take as much time as you need," Avery said indulgently.

A cool night wind slapped his cheeks as Avery stepped out of the club. After the scorching days he'd spent in India, it felt like a blessing. He inhaled a deep breath. There was no place like London. He had visited scores of capitals in his travels. Not one could match London.

He tucked his Malacca cane under his arm and crossed Jermyn Street, which shimmered under a light coat of rain, reviewing his night's gaming. He'd emerged a winner, but it brought him no real satisfaction. The old saying "lucky in cards unlucky in love" came to mind. And he was deuced unlucky in love.

He frowned at the intransigent thought. Love, was it? Gad, still a romantic at the advance age of twenty-eight. Surely he should know better by now.

He reached Piccadilly and heard his name called by someone lurching across the street. He frowned and was about to turn away when he realized the inebriated soul was his father-in-law.

"Avery, my dear boy, knew it was you." Mr. Sidney Challerton clapped the earl on his shoulder. "The very person I wish to see. I've had a rum bit of luck and am in urgent need of fifty pounds. Could you advance me the sum?" He leaned heavily against the earl, almost losing his balance.

Avery caught his breath at the vile odour of ale emanating from Mr. Challerton's person. Not for the first time he wondered how such a reprobate could have sired such a lovely daughter as Viola.

"You should be home, Challerton."

"Nonsense. The night's young." Two bloodshot eyes glared at him. "You're not home, are you?" he demanded.

"No. Neither am I foxed."

"Now, don't you turn into one of the Clapham Sect, Avery," Mr. Challerton whined. "Never could abide their prosing on about the dangers of drink. They never imbibe, so how would they know? Now, about the fifty pounds..."

"If you go directly home, I shall send Thacker later in the week with the fifty pounds for you," Avery replied.

A crafty look crossed Challerton's florid face; no doubt he was ruing the fact that he had asked for a paltry fifty pounds.

"Obliged to you, Avery. If you could see your way clear to giving me more than fifty pounds I'd be even more obliged."

"I daresay you would be," his son-in-law replied cordially. "I recollect that I discharged all your debts when I married Viola and left you an allowance to tap into in the year I was gone. How comes it you find yourself in a fix now?"

"Pshaw, you can't have expected that paltry allowance to last. A man has expenses."

"I told you I wasn't going to allow you to hang on my sleeve."

"I'm not," Mr. Challerton said, aggrieved. "Have I done so any time this year?"

"No, probably because I haven't been in England all year."

"And if you had been I still wouldn't have hung about. I have my pride," Mr. Challerton said, drawing himself up. "You may keep your precious fifty pounds. I won't be crawling to you, my lord."

He turned on his heel. Avery watched him stagger off, tempted to go after him. But any offer of help would be refused. It was obvious from whence Viola had inherited her stiff-necked pride.

He sighed. Like it or not, the fellow was Viola's father. He would have Thacker speak to Challerton and find out just how deep in dun territory he was running.

At last Avery entered Berkeley Square and approached his residence. The street was deserted, the only sound that of his footsteps.

No, not only his footsteps. His acute hearing detected another sound coming from the shadows. Coming fast. Avery's hand tightened on his cane and he swung, crashing the wooden stick down hard on top of the footpad's head.

"He's crushed me bleedin' 'ead!" the robber moaned, falling back onto the ground.

Avery whirled. The robber had been speaking to a second party. And there he was. A quaking, shaking runt of a thief holding a pistol aimed straight at Avery's heart.

"Your purse. Your money. Give it 'ere."

Avery dipped a languid hand into the folds of his coat. He brought out his purse and with a flick of his wrist tossed it at the second fellow. Instinctively the robber reached for it.

With lightning quickness Avery's cane banged against the robber's wrist. A howl went up. The pistol dropped to the ground. A swift kick of the earl's long leg and the weapon was out of reach.

Wasting no time, the robber turned tail and ran down the street. Grim-faced, Avery headed back towards the first robber, who had been moaning on the ground. But he too had fled.

Avery picked up the pistol and eyed his cane sadly. Broken. What a pity. It was quite his favourite. He stepped up to the door of his Town house and then was nearly bowled over when it opened and Viola rushed out in her night-dress, wielding a silver teapot.

"Richard, it's you!" she said.

"Good evening, Viola. Are you preparing to make tea for someone?" he asked.

She glanced down as though noticing the pot in her hands for the first time. "Oh, good heavens, no. It's the housebreakers. I do believe they are close by. I heard such noises."

He could not keep a smile from his face. She made such a curious sight in her dressing-gown with that teapot. "No one is breaking in. But let's go inside before you catch your death." They stepped together over the threshold into the warmth of their residence. "What were you going to do with that teapot?" he asked.

"Smash it over their heads, of course," she said stoutly. "It's very heavy. I would have taken a pistol from your library, but I knew you would dislike that."

"Under the circumstances, the teapot seems an appropriate compromise," he drawled. "A pity there was no opportunity to inflict damage with it."

"Yes, but I heard something, didn't you, Avery?"

"What you heard were two footpads trying to rob me."

"Rob you!" She became aware of the pistol he was holding in his hand. "Where are they?"

"Gone. I dispatched them."

She did not appear impressed with this feat. "Oh, no. They might have been the housebreakers. I did want them captured," she said. And she wanted to be the one to capture them.

"I don't think these two were the culprits plaguing the Square," Avery said. "They seemed more interested in my purse than my house." He put the pistol down on the ormolu table in the hall.

"Did you see them, Richard?" she asked eagerly. "Could you describe them?"

"It was dark and they came at me from behind," he said, considering the questions. "They were ragged and dirty. That's about all I can remember at the moment."

"Perhaps you will remember more tomorrow," she said as the case clock in the hall gonged the three o'clock hour.

"Tomorrow is today," he said with a yawn. "You'd best go back to bed." He picked up the oil lamp which Briggs had left for him. The light illuminated his face.

"You're hurt!" she exclaimed.

He dabbed at his cheek. "A scratch."

"But it must be cleaned. Come into my sitting room."

She seemed to take his acquiescence for granted and bustled about, gathering a basin of water and a handkerchief. Avery sat down in front of her dressing-table. The scrape on his cheek was not deep, but she insisted on cleansing it with soap and then rinsing it.

"There," she said, pressing a clean handkerchief to the small wound. "Hold this against your cheek."

"Thank you." He'd much rather hold her against his cheek. "Your touch is gentle," he said.

The intent look in his blue eyes gave Viola a moment's pause. Perhaps it had not been such a good idea to have invited him into her private rooms.

While she had been intent on ministering to his wound, she had not noticed the sour odour of rum emanating from his person. But now, as he drew closer, she did. She could not help shrinking from him. Avery felt her withdrawal. She did not want him. She had another. He rose from the chair.

"Good night. Sleep well."

He knew that once again very little sleep would be his reward.

"OH, MISS VIOLA, such a wicked world this is," Polly said the next morning as she drew back the drapery round Viola's bed.

Her mistress, blinking at the blinding sunlight, knew exactly how wicked the world was, in particular an abigail who did not allow her employer to sleep past nine.

"Heavens, Polly, close the drapes. I need my rest."

"Too much sleep will just make you knaggy. You don't want to be late for church. And don't you want to hear the news? Two more houses have been robbed."

Viola threw back her coverlet and sat up, all attention now.

"Briggs got it straight from the butlers of the two houses. The Donaldsons and the Vances. In an uproar they were."

"I can well imagine," Viola said, changing out of her night-rail and into a simple blue muslin. Really, the culprits were getting entirely too bold. They must be stopped. She felt more certain than ever that the two footpads Avery had fought were the housebreakers.

If he would only describe the men to her, she could draw a sketch and use it to make her enquiries.

Quickly she opened the door and peered into the hall. James, the footman turned valet, was carrying a breakfast tray meant for his master.

Viola smiled at him. "How is his lordship feeling?"

"Not the top of the trees, my lady. He refused my help shaving and then nicked himself on the chin."

"How disagreeable. I need to speak to him, James."

The servant looked alarmed. "He's not dressed yet, my lady. May I convey your message?"

"No. I wish to speak to him myself."

To storm a gentleman's private rooms was simply not done, and yet he had come into her private rooms last night. She surely could go into his. He was her husband, after all.

"Stand aside, James," she said, squaring her shoulders.

"My lady," James said, attempting to bar her path to the door. "I advise you not to enter."

"I shall take full responsibility."

James knew that the thin thread of a chance he had to succeed Walter as the earl's valet would be stretched to the snapping point if he allowed Lady Avery entrance. And yet he could not stand in her way, either.

Flushed with victory, Viola entered Avery's private rooms. The earl stood, frowning in a mirror.

"James, where are the dratted linen cloths?" he called over his shoulder.

"Have you used all of them so far?" Viola asked, following the sound of his voice.

Avery whirled round, speechless. He was dressed in his pantaloons with his white frilled shirt unbuttoned and baring a thatch of curly black hair on his chest, the sight of which made Viola feel a trifle faint.

"What are you doing in here!" he thundered. "Where is James? He calls himself a valet? I'll wring his neck."

"Don't blame poor James, Avery. He was in a quake because I rode roughshod over him to get in here. I might remind you that *you* have set foot in *my* private rooms."

"Never while you were dressing," he said.

"Let's not talk nonsense," she said briskly, averting her eyes as he buttoned his shirt. "Let us be sensible."

"I am not dressed for conversation, madam," he said, "sensible or insensible."

"I shall turn my back," she said, promptly doing so. "Does that alleviate your qualms? I simply had to speak to you about the housebreakers."

"Do you still have that maggot in your head?"

"It's not a maggot. Two more houses have been broken into."

Avery slid the last linen cloth round his neck and began his expert manipulations.

"I do think that if you tried to remember you could better describe the two who attempted to rob you."

"To what purpose?"

"To the purpose of apprehending them," she said.

"You'd best leave that to Bow Street. I shan't waste my time or theirs describing my assailants."

"But you could describe them to me, couldn't you?" she coaxed. "What if they should break in to this household? I should be in a terror."

He threw back his head and roared. "You needn't pitch that gammon at me, my dear. You were not in a terror at all last night. In high gig would be more the ticket. Indeed you appeared sorely disappointed that you couldn't crash my mother's favourite silver teapot down on their heads."

"That was last night, my lord," she said with some dignity. "Now that I have had time to reflect on the matter, I see how much danger I was in. I should like the villains apprehended and would have no compunction in doing so myself.''

''I believe there is a reward offered, isn't there?'' he asked, walking over to her so they were once again face to face.

''Yes, I believe so,'' she said, attempting a casual air. Money was of little concern to Avery. He'd laugh at a paltry twelve hundred pounds. But it would give her the start she needed in her new life as a governess.

''Don't you want the culprits caught? Describe them to me.''

Avery turned back for one last look in the mirror. The cravat would have to do. He shrugged on his coat. So his wife wanted to play Bow Street runner, did she? He would see to it that her search was in vain.

''Not very. Quite short.'' He indicated his shoulder.

''Colour of hair?''

''Dark.''

''Black like yours?''

''Hard to say. It was night.''

''You must remember something. Think.''

His brow furrowed. ''One was hunchbacked, I believe. And the other wore a patch over one eye. He also walked with a limp. The hunchback had a tattoo on his arm. I saw that plainly when I crashed my cane down on him,'' he said, fabricating wildly.

''What kind of tattoo, sir?'' Viola asked, frowning.

Tattoo…now what kind of tattoo should he give his imaginary thief? His lips curved in a smile.

"A cobra, ma'am, coiled and ready to strike."

"Now, let me see if I have this correctly. The thieves were a pair about my height, one with an eyepatch and a tattoo."

"No, the hunchback had the tattoo. His partner looked like a ferret."

"I thought you said he had one eye."

"So he did, but he still looked like a ferret."

"You are roasting me!" she accused, laughing despite herself. "I thought for a moment you were in earnest."

"Oh, I had you going on for considerably longer than a moment, minx," he retorted, his face softening with laughter.

"The shabbiest trick, Avery."

"It's all that you deserve for invading my rooms."

"Still I wish you had seen something. I would have liked to have claimed the reward."

He said nothing for a moment. But the laughter in his heart disappeared. Viola might be charming and more self-assured than when he had left England, but she was still as money-hungry as the day she had married him.

CHAPTER EIGHT

VIOLA THREW WIDE the doors of her wardrobe and eyed the finest silks and satins within with acute dismay. There was nothing whatever a governess might wear during the day.

It was particularly disagreeable since today, Monday, Avery would be attending an auction at Tattersall's, allowing her ample time to take tea at the Rose Garden in Piccadilly.

She fingered the rich gold embroidery on a dress hanging in front of her. What she needed was a plain dress in brown or grey. Ten minutes later she found exactly what she wanted on her abigail's back. Polly's dress fitted Viola's requirements to perfection: dark brown and devoid of ornamentation. And the two women were of a height.

"May I borrow your dress, Polly?" she asked as the older woman bustled about.

Polly stopped and stared at her as though she'd gone daft. "Borrow which dress?"

"The one you have on. Or shall I simply purchase it from you? Would ten pounds be enough?"

"Miss Viola, do stop your teasing. You know that ten pounds would be too much. You may have it for the asking but I cannot imagine what you would want with it."

Viola racked her brain for a suitable explanation. "It is for an amateur theatrical," she said at last. "You know Lady Dixon's fondness for the stage. She has coaxed me into playing a role of a highly respectable governess."

"Well, then, I see no harm in it."

An hour later garbed in Polly's brown dress and a pair of plain and sensible shoes, Viola entered the tea room in Piccadilly.

All the customers were as plainly dressed as she was, but they ranged in age from quite young—even younger than her own twenty-four years—to a comfortable middle age. Viola was soon seated at a small corner table. A yellow daisy floated in a small china bowl in the centre of the pink tablecloth. Viola scanned the menu. What should she order? Just the tea, or perhaps a plate of biscuits?

"Try the Chinese blend—it's ever so fragrant," a woman at a nearby table suggested with a smile.

"Thank you, I shall. Would you care to join me?"

The woman readily transferred her cup and saucer and teapot to Viola's table. She was young and slim with ginger-coloured hair and moved with an easy grace.

"I haven't seen you here before," she said, settling into the chair opposite Viola.

"No," Viola said. "I'm new to Town. I heard that this was a good place to visit if I wanted to meet other governesses."

"So it is. I'm Sarah Hawkins."

"Vi-Violet Brown."

Sarah laughed as they shook hands. "Violet Brown, what a colourful name. In whose household do you work?"

"I'm looking for a position at the moment. What about yourself?"

"I work for Lord and Lady Brightly," Sarah said proudly. "They have three children. Two girls, four and five, and one boy, two years old."

"A lively brood," Viola murmured.

Sarah laughed. "Yes, but the Brightlys are not as odious as some. I know I'm lucky."

Sarah was soon confiding to Viola that her position was just temporary for a year until Edward, the younger son of a Devonshire squire, finished his schooling.

"His father has promised to secure him a position in orders. When he does, we will be married," she said, beaming happily.

"Have you heard mention of anyone requiring a governess right now?" Viola asked.

Sarah shook her head, then her face brightened. "There is Miss Dawson just come in. I expect she may know something. She knows everything."

The redoubtable Miss Dawson turned out to be a severe-looking woman of about forty-five who declared emphatically that there were no good positions anywhere to be had in Town.

"Be thankful for what you have," she said with a brisk nod at Sarah, who immediately chirped that she was grateful to the Brightlys. Miss Dawson's unflinching gaze next fell upon Viola, who announced that she didn't have a position to be grateful for.

"Ah, then that's a different story," Miss Dawson said grimly. "How many languages do you speak?"

"French and a smattering of German. I also play the flute."

"Flute?" Miss Dawson accepted this news with a jaundiced eye. "Not much call for learning the flute. Harp, yes, and the pianoforte."

"What about Mr. and Mrs. Tompkins?" Sarah asked. "I thought they were looking for someone."

Miss Dawson's nostrils twitched. "They are always looking for someone. Mr. Tompkins has a rakish disposition," she explained to Viola.

"Oh, dear, I wouldn't want that in my employer."

Miss Dawson set her lips in a straight line. "All it takes is to be firm about things. No gentleman has ever dared to press his advances on me."

Fortunately, before Viola was obliged to respond to this, her tea arrived. She poured the brew out and inhaled its fragrance. It was as inviting as Sarah had predicted. By the time she had finished her second cup, two other governesses had joined their table and a gossipy exchange about the break-ins soon ensued.

One of the newcomers was Miss Headly, the Harding governess, who regaled the other women present with the stories of the depredations she'd suffered at the hands of the Runners.

"Treated as though I were a common criminal. Such questions." She took a deep sniff of her hartshorn.

"So disagreeable," Sarah murmured soothingly, patting Miss Headly on the back. "Do not fret about it."

"What did they ask you?" Viola could not help inflicting her own question on the much-harassed Miss Headly. She might glean a clue from the Harding burglary.

"Everything," Miss Headly said, ticking off the questions on her fingers. "What time did I retire to bed? Who usually rose first in the morning? Did I know where Lord Harding kept his cash box and Lady Harding her jewels?"

"Such impertinence." Miss Dawson crunched a biscuit between her strong teeth. "I wouldn't allow them to bullock me that way."

"I had no choice," Miss Headly said.

"Nonsense. You must look them straight in the eye and tell them they are being uncivil."

"That is easy for you, Ernestine, you are so authoritative. Things are more difficult for the rest of us," Sarah offered.

"Nonsense. Just screw your courage to the sticking point, that's all, Miss Headly. We can't have you running back to your mama like Catherine Pitts when her household was broken into.''

''The Morelys haven't found another governess since Catherine left, have they?'' Sarah asked with a look at Viola.

''Miss Brown wouldn't wish employment there,'' Miss Dawson said.

''Another rakish gentleman?'' Viola enquired, reaching for a lemon biscuit.

Miss Dawson sniffed. ''Mr. Morely is not haut ton. He has ties to trade.''

Viola, however, was not put out by such news. Dorothea was undoubtedly right about the enormous drop from a countess to a governess. It would be awkward to take up such a position in the household of someone who had known her as Lady Avery. But someone not in the first circle of Society would know nothing of her former identity.

The conversation soon turned to tonics favoured by employers: Miss Dawson touting Doctor Elcot's Tonic while Miss Headly preferred Doctor Rubin's.

Customers drifted in and out of the tea room. Viola noticed a dark-haired woman in a red blouse and flowered skirt who every now and then came through the drapes of the back room and walked past the tables. Frequently she would be invited to sit down with a customer.

''Who is she?'' Viola asked Sarah during a lull in the debate over tonics.

"Oh, that's Zorah, the Gypsy. She reads fortunes in our cups when we're finished. It's so amusing. Would you like her to read yours?"

"No," Viola said quickly. She did not really believe in the powers of fortune-tellers, but if the woman did have the gift of second sight she might discover that Viola was not an ordinary governess.

"I don't consider it so amusing," Miss Headly said, overhearing Sarah's remark. She brushed crumbs off the tablecloth. "Catherine Pitts had Zorah read her teacup, and the Gypsy saw trouble ahead. She wouldn't tell Catherine exactly what would be the trouble. The poor thing fretted about it so much she prevailed upon me to come with her for a private reading. Zorah told Catherine that trouble would arrive, but if she went away all would be well."

"That came true," Sarah said. "The Morelys were robbed. And Catherine did go away."

"Did she tell your future, as well?" Viola asked Miss Headly, who shook her head firmly. "No. I don't believe in such stuff and nonsense."

"How much did she charge for a private reading?" Sarah asked, twirling the strings of her reticule about her fingers.

"A pound."

Miss Dawson fixed a stern look in Sarah's direction. "Are you thinking of a private reading, Miss Hawkins?"

Sarah blushed. "I really don't know."

But when the Gypsy approached their table, Sarah bade her take a chair and offered her teacup for the first reading. The Gypsy's hooped earrings swung lightly as she peered into the cup.

"I see a young man," she said.

"That's Edward," Sarah agreed eagerly.

"He is separated from you. I see another man, older."

"His father."

"He stands between you."

Colour drained from Sarah's cheeks. "He does? He's always acted quite friendly to me."

The Gypsy shook her head. "I see your young man growing further and further away from you."

"Oh, no!"

"Stop this!" Viola exclaimed, the note of authority in her voice so ringing that those seated round the table stopped and stared. She knew this was not how a governess would address anyone, but she didn't wish Sarah to become more upset.

"You are frightening Miss Hawkins," she said to the Gypsy now.

"No, lady, I do not frighten. I just tell the truth about the future. I will look in your cup." She reached for Viola's, but Viola held back the porcelain cup.

"I do not want my leaves read."

"Why not?"

"I don't intend to be frightened witless by silly stories." Viola dumped the tea leaves back into the pot.

The Gypsy shrugged. "There are always some that disbelieve. Who else wants to know her future?"

Miss Dawson pushed her cup at the Gypsy. "Read mine. I don't frighten easily."

Sarah left the table and retreated to her original chair. After a moment Viola followed.

"Don't fall into a pelter," she soothed the ginger-haired governess. "Edward's father isn't scheming to keep you away from him."

"You are very kind to say so," Sarah said, blinking back tears. "But I know that Edward could look much higher for a bride. There was a young lady who set her cap at him and even tried to cast out lures. I used to think it was amusing. But what if she has convinced Edward's father that she is the proper wife for his son?"

Nothing Viola said would calm Sarah, and the young governess went off to arrange a private reading later in the week with the Gypsy.

"It's all fustian," Miss Dawson warned when Sarah returned.

"I must know the truth."

"Then I shall come with you to the reading," Miss Dawson said. "Best to be protected, in case the Gypsy tries to swindle you."

"Oh, that is kind of you," Sarah said.

Even Viola's misgivings were calmed. The Gypsy would think twice before attempting to hoodwink Miss Hawkins while the redoubtable Miss Dawson remained in the same room.

"Two hundred pounds," Avery's voice announced the bid in the auction room at Tattersall's.

The auctioneer flashed him a smile. "We have the bidding started at two hundred pounds from Lord Avery. A prime Arabian, gentlemen. You'll not see his like again."

This hyperbole left the earl unmoved. He knew the Arabian would be a good addition to his stables and was prepared to bid the limit of five hundred he had put the horse's value at. He had every expectation of winning the bidding for far less. Most of the others in the room had wasted the ready with earlier purchases.

"Two hundred twenty-five." Across the room from Avery Viscount Duvane lifted his hand to signal his bid.

Lord Newton, seated next to Avery, stirred. "That's Duvane," he murmured.

Avery tapped his quizzing glass against his teeth. So Duvane wanted the horse, did he?

"The last bid is two hundred twenty-five," the auctioneer said.

"Three hundred."

"Three seventy-five."

The auctioneer swivelled his head towards Avery. The earl made a pretext of examining the horse again through his quizzing glass.

"Four hundred."

The roomful of gentlemen held their breath, looking towards Duvane either to increase the bid or fall silent.

"Five hundred would be the top price for the animal, Richard." Newton spoke in an urgent tone to his friend.

"I know," replied Avery placidly.

"Four hundred twenty-five," Duvane said, his cheeks flushed.

"Four fifty," came the earl's cool reply.

"Four seventy-five."

Duvane's declaration was accompanied by a thunderous look at Avery.

Avery remained expressionless, but inwardly he wondered just how badly his wife's *cicisbeo* wanted the horse. Thinking of Viola brought to mind the musical composition she'd written for the viscount. The earl tightened his grip on his glass. Duvane might win the horse, but not just yet.

"Five fifty."

"Richard, are you daft?" Newton whispered in his ear. "It's only worth five."

Avery made no reply, concentrating all his attention on the viscount.

"Five seventy-five," Duvane said thickly.

"Six hundred."

A murmur and much shaking of heads around the room greeted the earl's latest bid. The auctioneer rubbed his hands.

"Too dear," Newton whispered.

"Six fifty," the viscount countered.

Avery shrugged. "Seven hundred."

Lord Newton fanned himself with a program. Seven hundred for a horse worth only five! What could Richard be thinking?

"Eight hundred!" Duvane shouted.

Avery pinched a speck of lint from his coat. The auctioneer glanced nervously his way.

"Lord Duvane's bid is eight hundred pounds."

"Yes, I know," came the drawling reply. "And rather dear for a horse worth only five hundred."

The room exploded in laughter.

"Going once. Going twice. Sold for eight hundred pounds," the auctioneer rattled off quickly. His face white with rage, Duvane plowed through the crowd of men enveloping Avery.

"You ran the price up deliberately!" he accused.

"My dear fellow, all I did was bid for the animal," Avery retorted. "I finally realized the folly of bidding so high for a horse which was only valued at five. Fortunately for me, I came to that realization sooner than you."

"I do not take this insult lightly, Avery."

"I do not mean you to do so." The earl meticulously flicked another piece of lint from his coat.

Duvane glared. He had not intended to buy the beast, but only to prevent Avery from achieving a bargain. But once caught up in the frenzy of the auction, he found his good sense had gone by the board. Now, once he paid off the eight hundred pounds, he'd need a long run of luck at the tables to keep his creditors satisfied. And Avery was to blame. *Blast him!*

132 THE ABSENTEE EARL

"My lord, there is the matter of the eight hundred pounds," the auctioneer was saying to Duvane as Avery turned away.

Lord Newton drove the earl back to Berkeley Square, still laughing over the trick Avery had played on Duvane.

"It wasn't a trick," Avery demurred. "A trick is deliberate, planned in advance. I hardly knew what I was going to do until I was doing it. You'll come in to nuncheon with us?" he asked as the carriage stopped in front of his residence.

"Only if you promise not to bore me with entreaties about Walter."

"Word of honour," Avery said blandly. "James might yet develop into a valet of renown."

Newton was not deceived by this praise of the footman. Still laughing, the gentlemen walked up the steps to the house. A young woman standing on the top step had apparently just sounded the knocker because Briggs had opened the door to her. The butler gazed now at the two gentlemen standing behind her.

"My lords, miss, do come in."

The woman turned, surprised to see the two men. She was a petite young lady, with a heart-shaped face and blond ringlets peeking out from her bonnet.

"Oh, dear. Did you come calling on Lord Avery, too?" she asked.

"Er, yes," Newton said, still in a jovial mood. "But you may see him first."

"Thank you," she said, crossing the black and white lozenges with them. "I just hope he doesn't eat me."

Newton exchanged a mischievous look with Avery. "Why would he?"

The woman bit her lip. "Do you know him well?"

"Intimately," the earl said, playing along with Newton's joke as he handed Briggs his hat and cane.

"I have heard he is cold and selfish. Would you agree?"

Hadrian winked at his friend. "Yes, by Jove. Avery's positively arctic."

"How came you by this description of him?" Avery asked, not about to be insulted under his own roof.

"From his wife."

"Well, if anyone can attest to his selfish side, it's Lady Avery," Newton agreed.

"What business do you have with Avery?" the earl asked, not liking the tone of this conversation. He wasn't as selfish as all that.

"I believe that is something I should be telling him, not you," the woman said in a voice of cool reproof.

"Oh, first-rate. Yes. Just so." Newton laughed.

"Hadrian, you are beginning to try my patience," Avery said.

The woman turned to Briggs, who was still standing by.

"Would you inform his lordship that Miss Miranda Symes, his cousin, is here to see him."

"His cousin?" Newton exclaimed. "I'll go bail it's been a devilishly long time since you've seen your cousin."

"I've never seen him, sir," confessed the young woman. "Except perhaps for a glimpse when I was a child."

"Then allow me the pleasure of introducing him to you. Avery, your cousin would like a word with you."

Miss Symes turned scarlet at the realization that she was face to face with the gentleman she had just stigmatized as cold and selfish.

"I am pleased to meet you, cousin," Avery murmured. "My memory is abominably bad; pray inform me if we expected your visit?"

"No—that is to say, cousin Viola told me that I could visit any time that Yolanda had no need of me," Miranda said, looking utterly confused.

"Ah, yes, Viola. And Yolanda doesn't need you?"

"Not exactly. It is rather a long story."

"Which we'd best hear over nuncheon," Newton said. He held out his arm to Miss Symes. "Let me escort you in."

Avery did not follow the others towards the dining room, turning instead to Briggs.

"Kindly tell Henri that we are sitting four to nuncheon in the small dining room."

"Very good, my lord."

"Where is Lady Avery?"

"In the library, my lord."

Avery walked quickly to the library where through the open door he spied Viola at his desk engaged in writing a letter. A lock of hair had fallen across her cheek. She looked utterly absorbed in her task.

"More household accounts, Viola?" he enquired, stepping in.

She glanced up, a look of surprise on her face. Not just surprise, he deciphered quickly, but also guilt.

She put the quill back in its stand, nearly overturning the ink-well in the process. "Pray forgive me for using your desk. I do apologize for such an intrusion."

"Not at all, Viola. You are welcome to use the library at any time. Pray continue with your letter."

"No. I have blotted the ink on the paper so many times."

She crushed the paper in her hand and tossed it quickly into the fire.

After returning to Berkeley Square and changing into her own clothes, Viola had been at sixes and sevens to discover a way to learn more about the Morely household.

Then she hit upon Mr. Thacker. Avery's lawyer knew far more people than she did. She had begun her letter, but she had instinctively destroyed it, knowing Richard would think it odd in her to write to Mr. Thacker.

"How was the auction?" she asked now.

"Quite enlivening," he said, his mind still on her correspondence. He'd wager a monkey she was writing a love letter to Duvane.

"Did you win the horse?"

"No. I was bidding against Duvane. I realized that he wanted the animal more than I did, so I let him have it. I remembered what a friend he has been to you."

She was taken aback for a moment. "That was kind of you, Avery."

His lips curved in a half smile. "Something I am not usually?"

"I didn't say that!" she protested.

"But you did say I was cold and selfish. At least that is what Miranda tells me."

"Miranda?"

"Yes. Cousin Miranda is in the small dining room with Newton. I came to inform you. She has, it seems, temporarily escaped from cousin Yolanda's clutches and landed at our front door."

CHAPTER NINE

IN THE SMALL DINING ROOM, Lord Newton was busy entertaining Miranda with tales of the various larks he and Avery had kicked up over the years. The most unlikely of these involved swimming in the Serpentine in the midst of a frigid February two years ago.

"Why would you do such a thing?" Miranda asked.

"A wager was at stake. The winner was whoever could stay in the longest."

"And who laid claim to this dubious distinction?" Viola asked, sailing in on Avery's arm and enfolding Miranda in a scented embrace.

"I did," Hadrian declared promptly.

"Dreamer!" the earl hooted. "I was in for considerably longer than you."

"Richard, your memory is the worst in London. I assure you that I won. I even remember my time was five minutes and thirty-two seconds."

"Fustian! I won the bet with six minutes even."

Viola chuckled to see her husband reduced to the status of a squabbling schoolboy with his friend. While the gentlemen were still arguing over the finer points of the wager, the ladies sat down to a table of cold chicken, ham and assorted sweetmeats.

"What a wonderful surprise to see you," Viola said to Miranda.

"I couldn't abide Yolanda's superior airs any longer," Miranda confessed.

"No, quite detestable, I'm sure, to be obliged to fetch and carry for her. But you shall have a lovely visit with us and go back to Devonshire much restored."

"I'm not sure I wish to go back," Miranda murmured.

Viola's brows raised. But she had no further opportunity to quiz her visitor because Lord Newton was challenging Avery to another swimming match.

"In the Serpentine again come winter."

"Done, by Jove!" Avery agreed, thumping his forefinger against Newton's too-broad chest.

"Good gracious," Viola intervened. "You'll perish of the cold, the pair of you."

"At least this way he'll spend this winter with his wife and not gadding about the world," Newton said, oblivious to the thundercloud look on his friend's face.

"Richard, Miranda has not seen London since she was a child," Viola said, covering her own embarrassment at Newton's gaffe. "We must make arrangements to have her see everything. The opera. Drury Lane. Almack's. Vauxhall Gardens. The Tower. The Zoo."

"You must allow me to help escort your cousin," Lord Newton said at once.

"I don't know if I want my cousin escorted by someone with a memory as addled as yours, Hadrian," Avery retorted.

Newton turned his good-natured countenance towards Viola. "Lady Avery, I appeal to you."

"We shall start with a tour of London tomorrow," Viola said. "You may escort us if you like, my lord."

"It shall be my great honour," Newton said.

Later, after Newton departed, Viola showed Miranda to her room and sat on the side of the bed, watching while Polly unpacked Miranda's small satchel. When they were alone again, Viola demanded to know just how horrid Yolanda had been to Miranda.

"No more than her usual," Miranda acknowledged, sinking into the goose-down mattress. "But I couldn't help thinking what you had told me months ago about London and the opportunities here."

"To be sure. There are so many things to see and do," Viola agreed.

A furrow deepened on Miranda's forehead. "I was thinking more of people to be met," Miranda confessed.

"Well, the Regent has already left for Brighton. But you will see several high-ranking persons at Almack's. I shall apply to Lady Jersey for vouchers for you."

"Actually, Viola," Miranda confessed, "what I would like is what you have."

Miranda's words took Viola aback. "What is that, pray?" she asked.

"I find I like cousin Avery very well and would not mind at all marrying someone like him."

"Someone like Avery?" Viola nearly choked on the words. Her guest had no notion of the problems marriage to someone like Avery brought. Someone *unlike* Avery would be more the thing for connubial bliss.

"I did not know you were that enamoured of the idea of marriage, Miranda. Last year you told me a comfortable spinsterhood was what you envisaged for the rest of your days."

"Yes, I know." Avery's cousin hung her head. "In truth, I've always been interested in marriage. I am female, after all. It's just that Papa never could afford a Season for us. Do you think it idiotish of me, Viola?" She looked up and blinked back tears. "After all, I am twenty-six."

"That makes you only two years my senior," Viola pointed out. "Hardly at your last prayers. And of course it is not idiotish of you to dream of marriage. Are you certain you wish marriage with someone from London? Perhaps a more convenient match could be made in Devonshire with someone you know."

"Yolanda believes that Mr. Leonard would be a perfect match," Miranda revealed in accents of loathing.

"So you have had an offer!"

"But I don't want Mr. Leonard." Miranda's eyes were no longer teary but angry. "I can't abide his breathing."

"His breathing!" Viola said, greatly astonished. She was prepared to help Richard's cousin, but this seemed a freakish whim, indeed.

"All people must breathe, Miranda," she said gently.

Miranda laughed. "Oh, I know. I don't mean ordinary breathing. It's just whenever we're partnered during a dance and the music brings us together he breathes on my neck and my flesh crawls. He's odious and fifty and fat. I won't marry him."

"Then we shall just have to find you someone else," Viola said, and on that optimistic note went off to locate her husband.

After a search which took her to the book room, music room and two drawing rooms, she discovered her husband in his dressing room, trying to instruct James about the particular polish which should be applied to his Hessians. Judging by the enthusiasm with which the valet greeted Viola, she believed the lesson was not faring well.

"That is putting it mildly, madam," Avery said acidly after James left. "I fear I am taxing his meagre wits."

"James is no slowtop," Viola said, taking up the cudgel in defence of the former footman. "But neither is he as needle-witted as you. Perhaps if you were to show him rather than tell him what to do."

"Show him?"

"Yes, by applying the shoe black yourself."

"Polish my own boots, you mean?" he asked, looking wholly astonished at such a suggestion.

"Well, just once," she said. "You say you did it the whole time you were away in India."

"That was different. Now I am returned and would like to enjoy the usual comforts of my home." He put his boots down, realizing with a jolt that once again she had invaded his private rooms, which was fast becoming an unsettling habit of hers.

"Did you wish to see me about something in particular, madam?" he asked.

"I've just come from a comfortable cose with Miranda."

"Excellent. I hope you deduced how long a stay with us she plans to make."

"No, I did not. But I do know why she descended upon us. Yolanda was quite horrid to her. She wanted Miranda to marry an odious farmer who was fat and fifty. Can you imagine such a thing?"

"An odious farmer who's fat and fifty. I certainly can imagine him." He closed his eyes a moment and put a hand to his brow. "I see him triple-chinned, balding and gouty. Probably possessed of the worst seat in the kingdom."

Her ready sense of the ridiculous bubbled forth at the image his words conjured up. "Wretch, how can you say such a thing," she said, laughing.

"Easily."

"Well, I'm sure that Miranda did not lodge any complaint against Mr. Leonard's seat. It was his breathing which she objected to."

"His breathing!"

"Yes, he breathed on her when they danced."

A look of disgust crossed the earl's face. "Clumsy bag pudding! I can understand why she took such a dislike to him." He paused. "Was it Miranda's purpose to find herself a husband who wasn't fat and fifty here in London?"

"She came to us in desperation, hoping that we would be kind enough to help her find a more suitable match."

"And what made her think we would be willing to enlist in such a scheme?"

Viola hesitated a fraction of a second. "I told her last year that she was a sweet-natured girl who would make any man an excellent wife," she said, making a clean breast of it.

"*You*, singing the praises of marriage? I find that difficult to believe. Particularly since I am such a cold and selfish husband."

Hearing her words once again from his lips brought an angry retort from Viola. "If I did call you that, my words were spoken in anger at being abandoned by you."

He was silent a moment. "Do you still consider them true?" he asked quietly.

She licked her lips, remembering the kisses he had bestowed there on the night of his return. By no stretch of the imagination could they be called the tepid favours of a cold man.

"Not entirely, sir."

Not entirely? Then which was he? Cold or selfish? Avery turned abruptly away from her, lest he prove the former wrong once and for all by taking her in his arms and kissing her senseless.

"I thought we should throw a small rout for Miranda and invite some congenial acquaintances of yours and mine," Viola said, turning the topic back to Miranda's visit.

The earl shook his head.

"You must see that to have any chance of attracting an eligible parti, Miranda must be put into the swim of things," Viola protested.

"I quite agree. The bigger a lake the better, don't you think? But not during freezing February."

"Are you still on about your wretched wager?" she asked, in a fog.

He grinned. "No, I'm talking about your wretched idea. You shall not throw a small party for Miranda, but a *grand ball*."

Hugely enjoying the look of bewilderment on her face, Avery helped himself to a pinch of snuff.

"A grand ball?" Viola gasped when she could speak. "I am not sure Miranda would be comfortable with an event so large."

"Is it Miranda you are concerned about or yourself?" he quizzed. "Perhaps you are unequal to the task of being hostess of the event?"

"I am equal to any task you lay before me," she declared. How dared he imply she could not fill her position.

His lips twitched in amusement. "Brave words, Viola. You are lucky I shan't put you to the test or you might find yourself swimming in the Serpentine with Newton and me next February."

"With any luck I won't be here next February."

The laughter vanished from his eyes. "Are you still thinking about that bill of divorcement, madam? Such matters always progress slowly. You might be married to me a good many years before any bill gets introduced into the Parliament. Now, I bid you turn your mind to this grand ball we are to throw for our guest."

A ball would give her something to concentrate on instead of this idiotish subject of divorce she was always trying to bring up, he told himself.

Indeed, Viola was already thinking of the ball. The grand ballroom would be used, of course. Briggs would know what to do, so she would rely on him. She would beg Susan's and Dorothea's help, as well.

"I trust you do not scruple at my hiring the best musicians," she said now.

"Not at all. Do the thing up properly. We'll have supper first, of course, for a select twenty of our guests. Draw up the guest list. Invite whomever you like," he said, "as long as that fellow Duvane is not among them. I will not countenance his presence under my roof, dangling after my wife or after my cousin. Have I made myself clear?"

"Why do you dislike him so?" She could not help asking.

Because you are too damned fond of him, a jealous imp inside him nearly replied. He squelched it immediately.

"The why is unimportant. Will you abide by my wishes?" he asked civilly, although they both knew it was not a question but a command.

DUVANE KNEADED the cramp in his left leg. He had been playing cards throughout the evening and now, with midnight fast approaching, he was still no further ahead than when he had begun. All Avery's fault. He should have been sitting down in White's comfortable card-room, instead of being forced to take a turn with the rabble frequenting this ramshackle, odoriferous Greeking establishment.

After the bidding war at Tattersall's it would be weeks before Duvane could approach White's without the tulips and pinks making sport of him.

He scowled down at the cards in his hand. He could have helped his luck with a convenient card up his sleeve, but the players sitting down with him were not the sort who would take kindly to such embellishment.

The viscount was growing rapidly more bored. However, the sight of Mr. Challerton sitting down in a recently vacated chair revived his spirits. Challerton was in his cups. He took no notice of Duvane's sleight of hand, which helped the viscount win several large wagers. At the end of just an hour, Challerton stood nearly a thousand pounds in Duvane's debt.

"A thousand pounds? Surely it's not that much." Challerton blinked his dissipated eyes.

"You can see your signature for yourself," Duvane said, holding out Challerton's vowels. "I shall expect payment soon."

"A thousand pounds. It will take me a few days to raise the funds." Challerton groaned to himself. He'd have a devil of a head tomorrow. He'd also have to endure a trimming from his stiff-necked son-in-law if he applied to him for help.

"You may take all the time you need," Duvane said magnanimously.

"Pon rep, that's decent of you, Duvane."

"I am not the ogre that some paint me," the viscount said with a deprecating smile.

"I'll vouch for that, sir. Best of fellows. I know I'll be able to make good the debt once my luck changes."

"Of course you shall," Duvane said encouragingly. "Do you want to try your luck any more tonight?"

"Why not?" Challerton said recklessly. Since Duvane wasn't going to dun him, there was no sense in turning down a civil invitation. Besides, his luck *could* always change.

MR. PETER THACKER stood on the Bristol dock Tuesday morning watching each passenger coming down the gangplank. On either side of him the milling crowd surged forward. Thacker patted his neck with a handkerchief. His employer had airily predicted that there would be no trouble recognizing Miss Neelah Garda, but Thacker was not so certain.

Finally, just as he began to wonder if Miss Garda had missed the vessel, a woman in a red sari with a red dot in the middle of her forehead walked shyly out from the boat. This had to be Avery's friend.

He pushed his way to her side.

"Miss Garda?" he asked, doffing his hat.

"Yes?"

"Peter Thacker, ma'am. Lord Avery's solicitor. He sent me to escort you to London."

She was quite young, probably no more than twenty, with the softest-looking cinnamon-coloured skin he had ever seen. Her teeth flashed in a brilliant white smile. Mr. Thacker felt himself dazzled.

"This way, please." He swung her satchel up in his hand and led her towards the waiting carriage. Avery had put one of his own coaches at Thacker's disposal.

"I ride in this?" she asked hesitantly.

Thacker nodded, finding her humility refreshing after the demands certain other females entrusted to his care by the earl had thrust upon him.

"It belongs to Lord Avery. He insisted."

"He must be the richest man in London."

"One of the richest," Thacker demurred.

"But definitely the kindest. I owe him my life. I would do anything for him."

Mr. Thacker said nothing to this, merely handing her into the carriage and taking up the reins, thinking all the while of just how Miss Garda would be repaying the earl.

A GRAND BALL: if that was what Avery wanted, that was what he would get, Viola told herself as she stepped into the grand ballroom with Lady Susan at her side. It would be more complicated than the simple routs she was accustomed to, but she had to do the thing up properly if only to prove to the doubting Avery that she could.

Lady Susan twirled about like a ballerina and clapped her hands with delight.

"Oh, what a marvellous idea Richard had. I have always loved this room. It is where I met Charles, you know."

Viola threw open a French window, while Susan stopped in the middle of the room, lost in memories of her girlhood many years ago.

"It was the night of my come-out. Papa gave a huge ball. Charles was one of the first gentlemen through the door. He told me later that he had glimpsed me on the street a year earlier and would have snatched me straight out of my schoolroom. I don't think I saw a handsomer man that night. You may laugh because he has gone grey now and has grown a trifle stout, but then he was quite the handsome beau. We danced twice, and the next day he sent me a bouquet of yellow roses, so many I could scarcely count them."

"How romantic," Viola said, feeling a stab of envy.

"I quite lost my heart," Susan confessed. "Although I didn't let him know that right away."

Viola cocked her head at her sister-in-law. "Why not?"

"Because gentlemen love a challenge, my dear," she said with a sibylline smile. "Why else would they be always wagering over cockfights or horrid mills or tramping up the Alps? Nothing is more boring than simply to throw yourself into their arms. It is important to appear less interested than you actually are. Ask them to repeat their words of ardour because you weren't listening, keeping them off balance."

"By all rights you should be telling Miranda this. I am already married."

"You are married to Richard," Susan said with a sidelong glance. "So it would behoove you to keep my advice in mind. Besides, I didn't keep poor Charles on a string that long. Just a month."

"So yours was a love match, Susan?"

"Oh, yes. Papa thought I was mad because there were even more flattering offers. Charles was a mere Mr. Worthing. But I was adamant."

Susan waltzed around the ballroom with an imaginary partner. "It's as grand as ever."

"And far more dusty than you remember," Viola said, running a finger over the wall. "Everything needs to be cleaned, from the floor to the chandelier."

"It seems generous of Richard to favour Miranda this way."

"He's not doing so for Miranda, precisely."

Susan stopped and stared. "Why else?"

Viola dusted her hands. "To show me that I am still the nervous chit I was a year ago, unable to fulfil my role as a countess by holding this grand ball."

"Fiddle; he'd be a gudgeon to suppose you incapable. Anyone blessed with eyes can see that you suit your position to perfection."

"Avery hasn't taken any notice."

Susan laughed. "Oh, yes he has. I know my brother, Viola. He thought that a year would make no difference between you. He could sail away and come back and all would be the same. I'm sure he's stunned to see how well you go about in Society. You don't really need him underfoot. That must be annoying to one as self-satisfied as Avery."

"I still don't know if I'm equal to this task, Susan," Viola said, deciding to open her budget completely.

"Of course you are," Susan said encouragingly. "It is only a silly ball. Just a bigger one than usual. I will be happy to assist in any way. You shall definitely need to hire more servants for the night of the ball and even the week before. When is it to be?"

"A week from Saturday."

"Have you compiled a guest list?"

"A partial one," Viola said, offering it now to Lady Susan's scrutiny. "I think two hundred people would be the limit of the room, do you not?"

"One hundred," Susan said. "If we want them to have room to dance."

"And he wants a supper beforehand for a select twenty."

"He would," Lady Susan said in accents of despair. "I can just imagine the howls that will go up over those precious twenty selections. Come along." Susan linked her arm in Viola's. "We shall throw the grandest ball London has seen and hang the expense!"

CHAPTER TEN

VIOLA SPENT the next two days up to her ears in plans for the ball. Whatever spare minutes at her disposal were given to Miranda. Together the two ladies climbed all one hundred steps of the Whispering Gallery at St. Paul's, visited Madame Tussaud's waxworks, and sampled the treats at Gunter's.

But these expeditions paled when compared to the one on Thursday to Madame Fanchon's shop on Bruton Street. The ton's leading modiste was scandalized by Miranda's countrified frock.

"She has not been walking out in public like that!" she shrieked.

"Now don't play a scene with me, Fanchon," Viola said, well versed in the famous modiste's histrionics. "You affected just such outrage last year when it was my turn to be gowned. You shall take Miranda in hand the same way you took me."

"*Bien sûr,*" Fanchon said. "I am glad to see you in that blue walking dress, my lady. Do you remember the discussion over the colour?"

"Yes, and you were right, as usual. Now you must turn your talents to helping Miranda. She will need several ball gowns and walking dresses."

"Oui, madame." Fanchon smiled radiantly at these words. "And for yourself?"

Viola paused as she fingered a bolt of emerald green silk on the counter. She had been too distracted with the details of the ball to think about what she would wear that evening. No hostess could appear dressed like a dowd.

"What would you suggest for me?" she asked.

Fanchon leapt at once for her sketchbook, showing her several new designs.

"Not Egyptian again?" Viola protested at one point. She'd had her fill of the Cleopatra style.

"Oh, no, *Madame,* not Egyptian but Asian."

"Asian?" Viola eyed Fanchon's sketch uncertainly. Avery had enjoyed a lengthy sojourn on that continent. Perhaps something in the Asian mode might pique his interest.

"From China comes the *cheong sam.* You see, a stiff collar like this, and gold Chinese frogs to button down the front and a slit up the side. What do you think?"

"I don't know. It is very daring."

Fanchon shrugged. *"Naturellement. You* are daring, *madame.* You cannot be wrapped in wisps of muslin, for a sophisticated lady like yourself can be a trifle more mysterious."

Viola laughed. "You will turn my head with your flattery, Fanchon. Very well. I leave it to you."

"I shall not disappoint you, *madame,"* the Frenchwoman said, looking pleased.

While Miranda was being measured, Viola thumbed through a copy of *La Belle Assemblée* and listened to the latest on-dits from Fanchon.

"Lady Brightly was just in, poor creature. She was robbed last night."

Viola looked up from her magazine. She had heard that name before. Where had it been? Then suddenly her memory cleared. Sarah Hawkins's employer.

Fanchon plied her tape round Miranda's waist. "Actually, they only discovered the robbery last night. It could have occurred anytime earlier."

"What do you mean?"

"They were out of Town." Fanchon paused to record the measurement of Miranda's waist. "For a sennight, and they just came back yesterday. Suspicion has fallen on their governess."

"Why?" Viola exclaimed.

"She was the only one other than the Brightlys who knew where they kept the jewels. Lady Brightly swore to that on the grave of her mother."

The grave of her mother, indeed! "But that is paltry evidence, Fanchon. It's far more likely the thieves just found the jewels by chance."

"*C'est possible.*" Fanchon nodded. "I didn't say evidence, *madame*. I said suspicion."

As soon as Fanchon had finished with Miranda, Viola hurried from the shop. Her first impulse was to set off straight away to the Rose Garden tea room and see what news the other governesses might have. But she couldn't go there dressed to the nines as Lady Avery.

Moreover, how would she explain to Miranda why she was at first oars with all the governesses.

Still puzzling over just when and how she could make her way unaccompanied to the tea room, Viola returned to Berkeley Square, listening with only half an ear to Miranda's chatter.

Their arrival back home coincided with Lord Avery's languid descent from his dressing room.

Viola could not help admiring his tall, elegant form even as she feigned amazement at his late emergence. "How now, Richard? It's nearly noon and you haven't had your breakfast."

"Unfair, Viola. If you only knew how eager I was to quit my dressing room. Unfortunately, James had trouble with the linen cloths. They should be starched and lightly ironed. It seems a simple matter which is beyond him. Then he was clumsy with his application of the champagne and the shoe black. The result was I ate breakfast off a tray. What, pray, have you two been doing, up and about so early?"

"We went to Fanchon's," Miranda explained.

"Getting ready for the ball," Viola said. She stepped away from Miranda for a moment. "Richard, may I have a word with you?"

"Certainly." He moved closer to her, inhaling the soft fragrance of her hair. Miranda went off into the music room.

"Would you be interested in a drive, sir?" she asked.

He gazed intently into her wine-dark eyes. "Is there some place you wish to go to?" he asked, twirling a lock of her dark hair round his forefinger.

"Not I. Miranda. Would you consent to taking her up in your carriage for a drive in the Park? It would add to her suitability to be seen with you, Richard. You must know your consequence is enormous."

He let drop the strand of her hair. "I'd as lief not."

"Really, Richard," she persisted. "Miranda is your cousin. You could take a deeper interest in her."

"I am throwing her a lavish ball next week," he pointed out.

"Yes, you are. But I am seeing to all the arrangements," she countered.

He cocked his head. "Are they too much for you?" he asked immediately. He had meant to keep her occupied but not to exhaust her.

"No. I am equal to the task! And it's not that I mean to pinch and scold you, but it seems a modest request to take her for a drive."

"Do you wish it that much, Viola?" he asked gently.

"Yes."

He nodded. "Very well, a drive it shall be." He started back up the stairs to change. "But just when I shall emerge from my dressing room, I cannot say." He flung the warning over his shoulder.

Despite Avery's gloomy prediction, it was only half an hour before his re-emergence, during which time

Viola had already informed Miranda of the honour in store for her.

"A drive with cousin Avery! Oh, Viola, won't you come with me?" Miranda beseeched her.

"Now don't fall into a pelter, goose. He won't eat you. Besides," she said practically. "The high-perch phaeton will only seat two."

"What shall I do? What shall I say?"

"Just be yourself," Viola whispered at the door. "And praise his horses and his handling of the ribbons. That is something all gentlemen take pride in."

After dispatching Avery and Miranda, Viola swiftly changed from the blue walking dress much admired by Fanchon into Polly's simple brown dress. She tied the strings of her oldest bonnet under her chin and, thus attired, went off to hail a hackney.

AT THE TEA ROOM, there was no sign of Sarah, but Miss Dawson was present, looking even more grim-faced than before.

"Ah, Miss Brown, isn't it?" The governess recognized Viola from their previous meeting. "In for a spot of tea?"

"Actually, I came hoping to learn more about Sarah," Viola said, seating herself at Miss Dawson's table. "I heard that her employers were robbed. Can it be true?"

"Aye," Miss Dawson said, sipping her tea. "Poor Sarah was questioned last night until she would drop.

She thinks the authorities believe she was in league with the housebreakers."

"But couldn't someone speak to the Brightlys on her behalf? Perhaps if you put in a good word for her, Miss Dawson—"

"Me?!" The self-assured Miss Dawson spluttered. "It's not really my place to tell Lord and Lady Brightly anything, even though Sarah is an honest soul and wouldn't steal a groat from them. But much they care about that. They even threatened to discharge her."

Viola drew a quick breath. "Can they? But that's so unfair!"

The Gypsy woman came out from the back room. Her large hooped earrings swung as she passed up the aisle, nodding to her customers.

"No one wishes Sarah misfortune," Miss Dawson said after a moment, "but perhaps you can benefit from it. You are in need of a position, are you not?" Her eyes narrowed sharply.

Viola nodded.

"You could apply to the Brightlys. They live at Number 12 Grosvenor Place."

"But Sarah is the governess there. I'd feel like a wretch to take her position from her."

"She won't be the governess for long," Miss Dawson predicted. "I'd be quick about it, if I were you. Others will be applying shortly."

Viola chewed on a biscuit. "Perhaps I will have a word with them," she said. But as Lady Avery, not Miss Violet Brown.

Zorah, the Gypsy, passed and nodded to Miss Dawson.

"Did you and Sarah ever have a private reading with that Gypsy woman, Miss Dawson?" Viola asked curiously.

"Aye. Sarah was much relieved to hear that she and her Edward would be reunited shortly. What fustian! There is no gift of second sight involved. She just got Sarah overset when she read her teacup and then calmed her nerves in the private reading. Meantime, she earned herself two pounds."

"You have a very practical view of things, Miss Dawson."

The other woman smiled, accepting this compliment with composure.

"I don't get myself into the fidgets the way some other females do," she acknowledged. "It never helps to fall victim to the vapours."

Viola sipped some tea. "I suppose the Gypsy's prediction did come true in a way. She will be reunited with Edward shortly. If the Brightlys turn her off she must return to her family."

"She'll return to her family. There's nowhere else for the poor soul to go. But I doubt she'll marry her Edward."

"Why ever not?" Viola asked, astonished. "Anyone can see she loves him so."

"The scandal," Miss Dawson said, with a sad shake of her head. "Sarah's Edward wants to take orders someday. He can't marry any female with a hint of notoriety attached to her. Duplicity in thievery?'' She pursed her lips. "No chance to hush it up, either, if I know Lady Brightly and her propensity for gossip."

Viola rose from the table. Somehow or another she must help Sarah. But how?

SHE RETURNED swiftly to Berkeley Square where a bewildered Polly was once again pressed into service to help her mistress change back into her elegant blue day dress. Viola was just rushing out of the door when Lady Dixon arrived for their driving lesson.

"Oh, Dorothea!" Viola exclaimed as she bundled her friend back down the stairs. "Pray forgive me. I am so shatterbrained that I forgot our lesson. But would you be so obliging as to drive me to Grosvenor Place? On the way back I could take the reins."

"What do you want in Grosvenor Place?" Dorothea asked, falling in willingly with this scheme.

Viola climbed into the barouche.

"To call upon Lord and Lady Brightly. Do you know them?"

Dorothea set her team of high-steppers off.

"Vaguely. With a sallow-faced daughter who is nearly out of the schoolroom. Not exactly in the mushroom class but not far from it, I hear. Where on earth did you meet them?"

"I didn't. I met their governess at that tea room you told me about."

"What a ninnyhammer I am for telling you about that place," Dorothea chastised herself. "I'd hoped by now you'd given up that ridiculous notion of becoming a governess.''

"I'm not going to Grosvenor Place to apply for a position, but to ask Lady Brightly not to turn off their governess," Viola said. Quickly she explained what had happened to Sarah. "Anyone who would dismiss sweet Sarah on the merest trifle is not the sort of employer for me."

"Just how are you going to stop them from firing your friend?"

"I don't know," Viola acknowledged. "I suppose I shall have to concoct a Banbury tale."

A few moments of furious thinking passed.

"What if I were to say that we are friends? That's not untrue. They wouldn't dare dismiss a friend of Lord and Lady Avery, would they? Particularly if that same lady were throwing a grand ball next week and was eager to have them attend."

Dorothea took her eyes off the road for a split second and nearly paid the penalty for it by crashing into a job-chaise. Quickly she pulled the vehicle to the left.

"Viola, you wouldn't invite such encroaching people," she said when she was once more in charge of her team.

"I certainly would if it means saving Sarah's job. What do you think of the scheme?"

"It might work," Dorothea acknowledged as they finally reached Grosvenor Place unscathed. "If they are toad-eaters, they will jump at the opportunity to show themselves at your ball, particularly with a daughter due to enter the Marriage Mart next year.''

Ten minutes later Viola and Dorothea were invited into Lady Brightly's red drawing room. Lady Brightly, a faded-looking woman with a vacuous smile, appeared dazzled by the appearance in her modest establishment of not only Lady Avery but Lady Dixon, one of the ton's premier hostesses. Cheerfully Viola begged Lady Brightly's pardon for descending on her without warning.

"I have a favour to ask you," Viola confided. "It concerns Miss Sarah Hawkins. She is your governess, is she not?"

"Why, yes. How are you acquainted with Sarah?" Lady Brightly could not keep herself from asking.

"She is a dear friend of my husband's cousin, Miranda Symes, from Devonshire," Viola announced.

Lady Dixon felt a tickle in her throat and hastily sipped the ratafia Lady Brightly had provided. A vile drink, but she managed to choke it down.

"Sarah is not from Devonshire," Lady Brightly pointed out.

"But Miranda is. And Yolanda. They are sisters, you see."

Lady Brightly did not, but her ambitions kept this remark from being uttered.

"How interesting," she said, fanning herself with a Chinese fan.

"My husband and I are giving a ball for Miranda next week," Viola pressed on to the crux of the matter. "Nothing would give Miranda more pleasure than having her bosom bow attend the ball. Of course we would tender invitations to you and Lord Brightly, as well."

Whatever Lady Brightly had expected this morning after the horrid night spent discussing the loss of her jewels, it was not to have an invitation bestowed upon her from the first circle of the ton.

"You would!" she exclaimed. "I mean, how gratifying, I am sure. We would be delighted to attend. I was telling Lord Brightly just the other day how handsome your husband was as he rode in the Park."

"Yes, and I am sure Sarah will be happy to hear the news, too. May I tender the invitation personally?"

Lady Brightly hesitated. "I'm not certain Sarah would want to attend a ball. She is very shy. But Brightly and myself would be more than happy to accept your invitation."

"I'm sure you would," Lady Dixon murmured so softly that only Viola could hear.

"Perhaps I could speak with Sarah," Viola suggested.

"S-speak to S-Sarah?" Lady Brightly stammered.

"If you don't mind."

Lady Brightly did mind, but far be it from her to say so to a countess. With composure, she left the room to search for the governess she had dismissed with ignominy just minutes earlier.

"What do you think Avery will do when he sees the Brightlys on the guest list?" Dorothea enquired.

"Nothing. He bade me take charge of the ball and that is what I am doing. I won't invite them to the supper beforehand, but lost in a crowd of a hundred they won't appear to such disadvantage."

"I hope you are right."

Moments later, Sarah appeared with Lady Brightly in the doorway of the red drawing room.

"Here is Sarah, Lady Avery," Lady Brightly said heartily.

Viola rose and crossed the room to the governess who dipped a quick curtsy. "Lady Brightly, may I have a word in private with Sarah?"

"Yes, of course."

Viola drew Sarah to the far corner of the room, separated by a garish gold-and-black oriental screen.

"I'm sure there's been some mistake, my lady," Sarah said softly. "Lady Brightly told me about the young lady I am supposed to be a dear friend of, Miranda from Devonshire, but I know of no one with that name."

"Sarah, it's me, Violet Brown," Viola said, taking her hand.

Sarah's blue eyes focused more intently on Viola's face.

"Miss Brown?"

"From the tea room. We met last week."

"Oh, heavens, what are you doing posing as Lady Avery?" Sarah asked, scandalized. "It is quite bad of you to play such a joke. Lady Avery is quite powerful, or so Lady Brightly says."

"Lady Brightly doesn't know anything," Viola said. "And I'm not posing as Lady Avery. I am she. Now, I know it is confusing, but just listen. I was at the tea room because Lady Dixon is having a theatrical in which I play a governess, and I had to see if my costume would pass muster. And you were so kind to me that I felt it incumbent upon me to try to help you when I learned about the theft last night."

"That is civil of you," Sarah said. "But I don't think even you can help me. Lady Brightly has discharged me."

"She'll hire you back."

"I know. She did just before we came in. But I don't think I want to stay in this household any longer. I thought they were the best of employers ... but to be suspected of thievery...." Sarah's eyes filled with tears.

Viola patted her hand gently. "Don't you think you could endure being a governess a little while longer? I daresay your lot will be much improved as my friend and Miranda's."

Sarah dried her eyes with a lace handkerchief.

"What do you mean?"

"Lady Brightly has a daughter due out next year. She won't want to anger me by dismissing a friend of mine until the chit is married off. All you need do is carry on in the usual way until Edward has entered into orders." And perhaps she could ask Avery just how exactly one went about securing a parish.

"But it seems deceitful."

"Would you rather face Edward with the gossip about the thefts?"

"No. Oh, no, never that."

"Now, don't be a goose. You shall go on just as you have here. And in fact, I do believe even better than before. You shall attend Miranda's ball next week. You shall be forced to endure the Brightlys for the evening, but we can't have everything."

Sarah's laughter smoothed the lines of worry from her face. "Thank you, Lady Avery. If there is anything I can do for you...."

"Well, actually, there is," Viola admitted. "Miss Dawson at the tea room told me the two of you had your private reading with the Gypsy. What happened at the reading?"

Sarah shrugged. "Not a great deal. Zorah had a crystal ball and bade us both look into it. I thought it was amusing, actually."

"That's all?"

Sarah thought for a moment. "She asked a few questions."

"What sort of questions?"

Sarah shook her head. "I can't remember. But nothing so difficult to answer. About Edward and me. She said some background information would give her more of a chance for a good reading, you see. I was quite nervous, but she eased my mind. Miss Dawson might remember more.''

''She says the same as you,'' Viola said.

And that she supposed was that. No one could ask for a more credible witness than Miss Dawson.

CHAPTER ELEVEN

"YOU WILL INFORM ME when this bogus theatrical of mine is set to run, won't you, Viola?" Lady Dixon's blue eyes twinkled merrily as she handed the reins over to her companion in the barouche. Viola had just finished confessing all to her friend.

"You are not too displeased, I hope?" Viola asked. It was infamous, she acknowledged, to have embroiled Lady Dixon in her schemes.

Dorothea waved a languid hand. "No, not in the least. However, I own to some curiosity. Just how do you plan to inform Miranda about this bosom bow she's never even met?"

Viola sighed. "I suspect I shall just have to tell her the truth."

"That would be a novelty."

Dorothea's teasing sparked a guilty pang within Viola's breast. She didn't like spinning tales, but if it was to help Sarah, she must. And perhaps the amateur theatrical need not be bogus.

"I believe you should hold a theatrical under your roof, Dorothea."

Lady Dixon threw back her head of guinea-gold curls and chuckled. "Does it have a part for a governess?"

"She is the lead, naturally."

The two ladies were still good-naturedly debating the merits of such a theatrical when Viola turned into Berkeley Square. The horses were going at such a fast clip that she did not see the phaeton approaching at the same time.

Her instructor did. "Look out!" Lady Dixon shrieked and tensed, preparing for the inevitable crash.

Avery, for it was he driving with Miranda, muffled an oath as he struggled to keep his carriage wheels from locking with Viola's. No one but a top sawyer would have succeeded in bringing his team of Welshbreds clear without injury.

"Oh, Avery, what a prime piece of driving that was!" Viola was moved to exclaim.

"I wish I could return the compliment, my lady," he said, struggling to keep his Welshbreds calm. "Is it your habit to allow a team to bowl around corners at such breakneck speed when you cannot control them?" he asked acidly.

"I would have if you hadn't been in the way," she replied. How like Richard to take offence from a compliment.

"I wasn't in the way. I had the road." He turned to Lady Dixon. "Dorothea, I am relieving you of your duties as my wife's instructor."

Dorothea took this demotion without a blink. "You would do better to learn from your husband, Viola," she agreed.

These words did not mollify Viola.

"You will be delighted to hear that Miranda was a great success in the Park today," the earl went on, handing Miranda down from the vehicle where she'd been sitting, saucer-eyed.

"Hardly a great success, cousin," Miranda demurred.

"At least five sprigs nearly trampled me rushing over to pay me their compliments and beg leave to be introduced to you."

"Were there really five?" Miranda asked. "They were charmingly droll. I particularly liked that blond gentleman, Duvane, wasn't it?"

Avery's smile faded. A stern look came over his craggy features.

"You'd do well to avoid him, cousin."

Later, when Viola and Miranda were climbing the Adam staircase, Miranda ventured a word about Duvane.

"There was nothing for Cousin Avery to take exception to, Viola. Lord Duvane acted with every civility."

"That's probably what put Avery's hackles up," Viola said. "For some reason Duvane is in his black books."

"Then he won't be at the ball?"

Viola shook her head. "Avery gave me strict orders not to invite him." Reminded in this fashion of her guests for the ball, Viola begged for a favour from Avery's cousin.

"But of course. Anything in the world," Miranda replied at once.

"A Miss Sarah Hawkins will be attending our ball," Viola said, finally reaching the top of the stairs. "She's a governess whose acquaintance I have recently made. It is deuced complicated. Do just listen . . ."

After several minutes Miranda grasped the full particulars. In order to allow Sarah to marry her beloved Edward it was necessary for her to continue governessing the Brightly brood for another six months. Lady Brightly would not dare dismiss her because she thought Sarah a good friend of Lady Avery and the earl's cousin from Devonshire.

Since Miranda possessed a romantic streak herself, she was more than willing to claim old friendship with Sarah.

"But you must point out this bosom bow when she arrives so I can recognize her," she said before going off to change from her riding habit.

ON MONDAY MORNING, footmen scurried about London delivering the cream-coloured invitations to the Avery ball. By the time Avery, Viola and Miranda stepped into Almack's Assembly Rooms on King Street Wednesday evening, the ball was on everyone's lips.

Those who had been invited were profuse in their thanks and lent quick assurances of attending, while those who had not been invited could only sniff and wonder why so much fuss was being made over yet another dismal rout.

Among those who felt the sting of being overlooked was Viscount Duvane. And he knew exactly why. Avery, not content with besting him at Tattersall's, was delivering him another facer by this pointed omission.

However, he was not entirely weaponless himself. Duvane's keen eyes did not miss Avery's possessive manner now, when the viscount stopped and greeted Viola, who was in her best looks this evening. The kiss he delivered on Viola's hand caused the earl to frown darkly. The viscount smiled to himself. He also recognized the look of consternation Viola gave to Avery.

So his attentions to Viola put Avery out of curl, did they? *Good.* Duvane bowed and sauntered away. He was content to wait his turn.

Later that evening, he saw his opportunity for mischief. Avery had, after much coaxing from Viola, led Miranda out in the quadrille. In languid fashion, Duvane circled the ballroom until he reached Viola's side, where he begged for one of the dances on her card.

"I'm sorry, Duvane, but I cannot."

"Cannot or will not?" he asked with a pointed glance at Avery, dancing with his young cousin. "Is your husband making presumptions about me? If so, you have only to say the word and I shall tell him to go to the devil."

"Oh, no. Don't do that!" She didn't want a duel between these two. "He only asked me to refrain from ... well ... flirting with you."

"My dear, I am devastated."

"You are? Now you are funning." She struck him playfully on the knuckles with her fan.

"You can ease my distress with a dance."

"Duvane, I can't," she said, uncomfortable with his persistence. "Pray don't ask me again. I dislike saying no to anyone."

The viscount laid a hand caressingly on her shoulder. "*Ma chère,* dance with me. Never mind your odious husband. He deserted you. Have you forgotten?"

"No. I haven't forgotten. But I think it best all the same not to dance with you."

A flicker of anger showed momentarily in the viscount's blue eyes. Never before had any woman resisted his charm so strenuously.

"You absurd child. We have danced before many times. What is one more? We shall call it our last dance before I bid you *adieu* with a broken heart."

His words brought a half smile to her lips, but she remained adamant.

"I'm sorry. My answer is still no."

He bowed, turned on his heel and stalked away. Stupid woman. He had showered her with attention during the months of her husband's absence and this was how she repaid him: with public humiliation. She was no better than her husband and certainly would receive no favourable treatment from him hereafter.

Indeed, the more Duvane dwelt on Viola's refusal to dance the more furious he became. He would extract his own revenge on both Avery and his wife.

Avery, for his part, had noticed Duvane pressing Viola to stand up with him and was pleased to see him stalk off alone. He led Miranda back to Viola's side and offered to procure refreshment for them both.

"None of those stale cakes or sour lemonade for me," Viola declared.

"Then I wonder why you wished to come here this evening," he asked as Mr. Samuels claimed Miranda for the next dance.

"Because of Miranda, of course," Viola said, plucking at the sleeve of her gown. "She must be seen by the eligibles in the ton."

"The eligibles seem to be in thin supply," he said, glancing about the room with his quizzing glass. "Can't remember when I've seen a more maggotty crew."

She choked on a laugh.

"Really, Richard."

"Are you sure you wish Miranda to wed one of them? Perhaps her fat farmer in Devonshire will be the victor, after all."

"Do stop your roasting. The gentlemen are just as they should be. Civil and polite."

"Yes, a sad want of dash among this younger generation," he lamented. He checked the next words on his tongue because the Countess Lieven sidled up just then, wanting to know where they would be spending the summer.

"I know Lady Avery spent last summer in Brighton. Do you plan to do so again this year?" she quizzed.

Viola flushed under this blatant inquisition; however, Avery was made of sterner stuff and blandly reassured the Patroness that they would indeed be repeating last summer's visit, with one difference.

"Viola shall be the one racketing about the Continent, and I shall be the one taking tea with the Bishop of Bath."

"You would be more likely to play whist for impossible stakes with the Duke of York's set," Viola said, following his lead.

"No stakes are impossible, my dear," Avery said with a careless laugh. Later, after Countess Lieven strolled away to speak to someone else, he vented his spleen.

"Odious biddy."

"Hush," Viola said, looking over her shoulder. Thank heaven the countess hadn't overheard. "You don't wish to turn her against us."

"Why not? We're already married. We have nothing to fear."

"Miranda."

"Oh, the devil. I forgot."

"Don't," Viola reprimanded.

"Well, I don't plan to allow the Patronesses to pinch and peck at me. There are too many of them and only one of me. Come, let's dance."

He stretched a hand out to her. Impulsively, she laid hers in it and they joined the throng on the floor. His hand clasped her closely around the waist, much too familiar a hold if they had not been married. But since they were, not even Mrs. Burrel, a high-stickler, could raise an eyebrow in objection.

The two moved together in the waltz as though they had been dancing it forever. In the crowded room the other couples gave way, allowing husband and wife to have the floor. A set of dizzying spins rendered Viola giddy and brought a spontaneous burst of applause from the onlookers.

Avery smiled down at Viola. Her eyes sparkled, her skin glowed. She'd never looked more radiant. He himself was feeling more content than he had in months. Was that her doing?

"Thank you," he said now to Viola.

"For what?" she asked, looking up into his penetrating eyes.

"For this waltz and for not dancing with Duvane. I saw him ask you."

"I was merely following your instructions, sir."

Had she only turned Duvane down because of that, the earl wondered, unsettled by her remark.

He fell silent a moment, loath to disturb the comfortable atmosphere between them and yet unable to suppress his curiosity.

"Am I to assume that had I not made my preference known that you would be waltzing with him instead of me?" he asked, giving in to his devil.

"Not exactly," Viola said, feeling flustered the way she often did when he pressed close to her. "I might be standing up for a quadrille with him," she teased.

His lips lifted in a smile, but his blue eyes showed no amusement. He must know just what Duvane was to her.

"Duvane did not take well to your refusal to stand up with him. It was unexpected?"

"I suppose so. I have danced with him before on many occasions."

"Indeed."

Those two syllables caused Viola to lift her chin defiantly. "I saw nothing wrong with dancing for amusement, sir."

"It depends on who you amused yourself with, madam."

She stiffened in his arms. "There has been not the slightest hint of impropriety between Duvane and myself."

"I'm pleased to hear you say that. You say it so often I am reminded of that old line of Shakespeare's. 'The lady doth protest too much, methinks.'"

"Only because her husband won't see fit to believe her when she speaks the truth," Viola said, nearly giving in to the temptation to box his ears. He had no cause to rip up at her. She almost wished she had danced with Duvane.

Thankfully, just then the waltz ended and Lord Newton came over to engage Avery in a discussion on the finer points of a valet's duties.

VIOLA'S TEMPER did not improve Thursday morning when she found herself sitting before a mound of bills for Miranda's ball. She had directed all the accounts for the ball to be sent to her before she dispatched them to Mr. Thacker for payment.

Since Avery had demanded she take full charge of the ball, she was determined to oversee every detail.

However, as the pile of bills grew higher with every day, she felt tempted to bundle them off and just deposit them on Mr. Thacker's desk. An efficient soul, Thacker would make quick work of them.

Resisting the urge, she lifted yet another bill from the top of the stack. This one came from the Carter Employment Service, which was supplying extra servants on the night of the ball. Her eyes skimmed down to the bottom of the bill, widening at the final sum. Far more dear than what she had expected. Could the fees have increased so much since the last time she'd used the service?

The wooden chair creaked as Viola leaned back and perused the bill more closely. After five minutes, the tiny frown on her brow had turned into a crevice.

She had ordered two footmen and three maids for the night of the party. Somehow, in addition to these five servants, an extra footman, butler and maid had been included on Avery's bill.

Unconscionable! She tallied the figures again and found the extra servants amounted to an additional hundred pounds.

How dared the Carter Service play such a shabby trick! She rose from her desk, determined to put a stop to this at once.

One hour later Viola climbed the wooden stairs leading to the Carter Employment Service. The office in the City surprised her by being spotlessly clean, and Mrs. Carter, the manager of the service, greeted her with every sign of civility, putting Viola in mind of a dignified, grey-haired schoolmistress.

"How may I help you, my lady?" Mrs. Carter asked.

"I have come about this bill," Viola said, taking it from her reticule and handing it across the desk. "You recognize it as your own?"

Mrs. Carter adjusted her pince-nez and scrutinized the paper. "Yes, of course it is ours."

"Good. Then I am confident you will find the error straight away."

Mrs. Carter bent her head over the paper on her desk. A minute later, she took off her glasses.

"I'm sorry, my lady—"

"I thought you would be," Viola said, unable to keep a note of satisfaction from her voice.

Mrs. Carter cleared her throat. "You misunderstand. I meant to say, I'm sorry but I find no error."

"Good gracious, the amount you have listed is wrong by a hundred pounds," Viola declared. "I ordered five servants for my ball on Thursday evening, but you put down an extra butler, maid and cook. What need do I have for an extra cook? Henri sees to all the provisions, and will be infuriated if anyone new invades his kitchen.''

''I am not in the habit of cheating anyone, my lady. If you will allow me to search a few minutes in my files for the answer.''

Viola drummed her fingers impatiently as Mrs. Carter immersed herself in more papers. Ten minutes passed. Then Mrs. Carter uttered a small cry of triumph.

''I see where the mistake was made, my lady,'' she said at last. ''The extra cook, butler and maid were hired at Mr. Thacker's request, not yours.''

Viola stared at the other woman. ''Mr. Thacker!'' she said thunderstruck. Why would Mr. Thacker concern himself with servants for her ball?

Mrs. Carter pointed at a ledger sheet. ''Here is where the mistake occurred. Mr. Thacker ordered the three servants sent not to Berkeley Square but Albemarle Street.''

For an awful moment, Viola went rigid while the office ceiling and floor spun wildly. Albemarle Street?

''Number 12 Albemarle Street, to be exact,'' Mrs. Carter said helpfully.

Viola drew in a slow, painful breath. There could be only one reason why a butler, cook and maid had been dispatched to an address on Albemarle Street by Mr. Thacker. Because his illustrious employer had bade him to do so. How unfortunate for Avery that the bill for his new *chère amie*'s servants had been added to the bill for Miranda's ball.

Viola's cheeks burned. How dared he? After denouncing Duvane as her flirt! If flirt he was, that's all the viscount had been, certainly not a lover. The injustice cut her to the quick. Avery felt free to take any bird of paradise under his protection, but she could not even dance with a friend.

How many people knew his Albemarle Street residence was again in use? She would be obliged to bear the sly innuendoes and pitying looks once more.

No, she wouldn't. Last year she'd been a mere country miss clinging to the tattered hope that when the earl returned, her marriage would somehow be put to rights. Now, he was returned and she knew it could never be right.

"Lady Avery?" Mrs. Carter's gentle tone roused Viola from her brown study.

"Mrs. Carter, what a goosecap you must think me. I most earnestly beg your pardon. My husband had mentioned that he would be hiring other servants for a house that his sister would be using on Albemarle Street. But I completely forgot about it."

"These things happen, my lady," Mrs. Carter said with composure. "We do run an honest service here. Many come to find employees and those in service to find reputable houses."

"I'm sure they do," Viola said, hesitating as another thought suddenly struck her. "I wonder if you might know anything about the Morely household, Mrs. Carter.''

''Morely?''

''Yes, I understand they are in need of a governess. The vicar's wife from my old village was asking me about the suitability of such a position for a young woman in the parish,'' she said, adding another Banbury tale to her list.

''Morely—that name does sound familiar,'' Mrs. Carter admitted, reaching for her files once more. ''Ah, yes,'' came the reply a few moments later. ''Indeed the Morelys have requested any suitable candidates for governess to be sent to them. They offer an excellent salary of one hundred pounds a year and have just the one child to be attended to.''

''Have there been many applicants?'' Viola asked.

Mrs. Carter nodded. ''Yes, but they are conducting a thorough investigation before they hire anyone. They were robbed not very long ago.'' Mrs. Carter's voice dropped to a confidential tone. ''I don't know if that young woman in your parish could bear up to the Morelys. Perhaps another household would be more to her liking.''

''Such as?''

''Would you like me to draw up a list of other available households in need of governesses, my lady? It will only take a few minutes.''

''Thank you,'' Viola said.

Ten minutes later, Viola had the list of available openings for governesses, which she folded and tucked neatly in her reticule. She would lose no time trying to fill one of those positions. The sooner she removed herself from under Avery's roof, the better.

Thanking Mrs. Carter and apologizing again, she left the employment office. Now to go home. She paused at the bottom stair, her hand holding the banister. *Home.* To her, home was no longer Berkeley Square. Nor was it her aunt's household. With a pang she realized that she *had* no home.

Feeling weary at heart, she climbed into her tilbury. How could Avery have installed a *chère amie* so quickly?

Perhaps she had misjudged him. Maybe there was no female present at Number 12 Albemarle Street.

Clinging desperately to this hope, she found herself at that very address. She had never seen the residence where, according to Charles Worthing, Avery had housed his high flyers during his salad days. But she had no difficulty recognizing it. Nor had she the slightest difficulty recognizing Avery's Town chaise parked on the flagway in front of it.

CHAPTER TWELVE

THE LAST TIME Avery stood in the small drawing room at Number 12 Albemarle Street, a flaxen-haired beauty had been hurling a Ming vase at his head. It came within ames ace of lopping off his right ear. He gave that lobe a tug now, devoutly thankful nothing of that nature would happen today.

Far from hurling vases, Miss Garda looked more inclined to hurl herself on the earl's broad chest.

"My rescuer," she said now, holding her arms outstretched to him.

He took one brown hand gingerly in his and shook it firmly, keeping the rest of her at bay.

"Too kind by half, Miss Garda. I do assure you. Any other Englishman would have done as much."

"That is not true," Miss Garda replied, her smile almost as brilliant as the bright-coloured sari she wore. "You set me up in this handsome house, hire servants for me and even put your excellent Mr. Thacker at my disposal. It is so generous of you, my lord."

"Nonsense. Just wish you to get a good start in England," he said, dropping her hand.

He poured a glass of Madeira for each of them from the tray of restoratives on the small sideboard, reflecting on the other beauties housed under this roof over the years. Before the flaxen-haired creature, there had been a redhead with a tendency to take snuff, before her a ballet dancer, and before her? He frowned, unable to remember just who had preceded the ballet dancer. Strangely enough, these amorous memories annoyed rather than pleased him.

"My lord Avery, you have done so much for me," Miss Garda said, sinking gracefully down on the velvet settee. "I am forever in your debt. Just tell me what you want and it is yours."

He sipped his Madeira, finding it inferior to the one Viola had chosen for him at Berkeley Square. He smiled across at Miss Garda. She was a comely enough woman, dark-haired, possessed of real beauty and spirit. If he made to seduce her, he felt certain he would succeed. However, he felt not the slightest inclination to do so. Was it just a chivalrous impulse because she was a foreigner in a strange land or was it because he was married to a spirited, dark-haired beauty whom he would much rather seduce if he could?

"There is no debt," he said rendered uncomfortable with the direction of his thoughts. Viola, blast her, still was inordinately fond of Duvane. "You may live here in Albemarle Street until you decide what you wish to do in England. I have directed Mr. Thacker to assist you in whatever way he can."

"Yes, I know," Miss Garda said. "Mr. Thacker has been so helpful. He is trying to find me an instructor to help me with my English."

"Splendid. You appear to be in good hands."

"Good hands?" She looked puzzled as she glanced down at her palms.

"You seem to be getting on very well," he amended. Miss Garda would find the tangle of English difficult enough to sort out.

He finished his Madeira, then took his leave, pleased that Miss Garda was comfortably settled. One less thing for Avery to worry about.

SOME TWENTY MINUTES earlier, a tilbury had made its way from Albemarle Street, the driver fighting back tears which blinded her to the real hazards of the road. More than one irate coachman shouted at her as she nearly caused an accident.

"Here now, Viola!" A familiar voice cried out, and she looked down to see her father waving her to a stop. Mr. Challerton had been on his way to cajole some badly needed funds from his daughter. And here she was, driving every which way like a greenhorn.

"Give me those reins," he said, climbing up beside her and taking them from her limp hands. "Saw you nearly run over that fruit cart. Rum bit of business, that. Where's your groom?"

"I don't need him, and where are you driving to?"

"I'm taking you back home to Berkeley Square. I was bound there to have a word with you," he confided.

Viola temporarily forgot about her own troubles.

"Oh? What did you want, Papa?"

Mr. Challerton's chin jutted out an inch, and he looked more aggrieved than usual. "What makes you think I want something?"

"Was it just a social call, then?" she asked ironically. "I do beg your pardon. It's just that the last two times I had occasion to see you, both times you were in Dun territory and desperate to borrow money."

Mr. Challerton felt a twinge of guilt. "I am not desperate to borrow anything, just hopeful."

"Ah, I see. A world of difference indeed, Papa, between hope and desperation."

"Hmmph!" Mr. Challerton snorted.

Viola gazed with affection tempered with sorrow at her father. As a child, she had at first adored her errant parent and then wondered at his continued absence. Even when she was sent to live with her aunt, she refused to think ill of him. It was only in the past few years that she was able to admit that her father's character was considerably flawed.

"Come now, Papa," she said more softly. "What is it that you want?"

Mr. Challerton's hands twitched on the ribbons.

"It's just that your husband hasn't seen fit to lend me the monies he promised. I applied to him last week, and he assured me that he would see to it right away. But I have been waiting and falling even deeper into debt."

"How much do you need?"

"Two thousand quid."

Viola clung to the side of her seat as the carriage hit a rut in the road. "I can't lend you such a sum, Papa."

"I'm not asking *you* for it," he expostulated. "But you could get Avery into a pleasant mood and coax him out of the money I need, couldn't you?"

Nothing was more abhorrent to Viola than the image of herself coaxing Avery out of anything.

"I won't do it," she said, crossing her arms on her chest.

Mr. Challerton sent her a wary look. "You would see your poor father thrown into debtors' prison?"

"I would prefer to see my father the man I once thought he was."

Mr. Challerton rubbed his chin. "You have every right to ask Avery for help. He's your husband."

"But not for long," Viola said, thinking of the mistress Avery had just installed at Albemarle Street.

Mr. Challerton turned pale. "What do you mean?"

Viola smoothed her skirts. "I mean, Papa, that I am taking steps to remove myself from this odious marriage."

"How now, how can you do any such thing?" her father demanded. "You're married to him, right and proper." He paused, not liking the expression in his daughter's violet eyes. "You're not thinking of a divorce!"

"And why not?" Viola countered swiftly.

"Because of the scandal, girl! You won't be able to lift your head up anywhere. No, no," he said, becoming quite agitated. The team he was driving seemed to sense his agitation and began to fight him round a corner.

"I am unhappy in my marriage, Papa," she murmured softly.

Mr. Challerton sighed. "Of course you are. You're not a schoolroom miss, Viola. Everyone at one time or another is unhappy in marriage. No reason to go running off to get a bill of divorcement introduced in Parliament. Make no hasty decision, girl. You're just having a lovers' quarrel."

Viola's laugh was bitter.

"Avery is certainly not in love with me. You shall just have to look for another way to pay your debts."

"I can't," Mr. Challerton said despondently. "It's too late to learn new tricks, my girl." He drove on in silence. "Do you remember when I was considering the offers you received last year?" he asked.

Viola nodded. How long ago that seemed.

"Lord Bantry had a tendre for you. He was an easy-natured soul with a purse larger than Avery's. I was willing to accept his offer, but you ranted and raved and said that Avery was the only husband you wanted. You stormed so much I thought you would have an attack of the apoplexy. You ended by wishing me to Jericho. Remember?"

Viola laughed.

"So I consented to accept Avery's offer, over my better judgement, mind," her father continued. "I knew his reputation for dabbling in the petticoat line. And now you tell me you don't want him for a husband. Do you know how many caps have been set at the fellow? How many females would have given their eye-teeth for one word with him?''

''I must take care to examine the teeth of the ladies the next time I am at Almack's,'' Viola said.

''Levity will be the ruin of you,'' her father said.

''You are mistaken, Papa,'' she replied. ''Levity is the only way I can keep my heart from breaking.''

Not wishing to have her transformed into a watering-pot, Mr. Challerton hastened on.

''Divorce ain't the answer, Viola. The gossips will prattle, and it's you who will bear the brunt of it, not Richard. He will still be the Earl of Avery. But after your divorce, you'll be nothing.''

''I don't care,'' Viola said in a voice of ringing steel. ''I won't stay married to him.''

Mr. Challerton was silent for a moment, chewing on his lip.

''I understand you are having a ball next week for Avery's cousin,'' he said.

''Yes,'' Viola said, lifting her head sharply, puzzled by this turn in the topic. Was her father on his high ropes because no invitation had come his way? ''I do beg your pardon, Papa, I didn't invite you because you never like such formal occasions.''

''That's right enough,'' her father agreed. ''Besides, I wouldn't fit your company. But would you consider inviting a friend of mine. He's not rag-mannered.''

''What friend is this?'' Viola asked skeptically.

"Duvane."

"Duvane?" Viola was startled. "I didn't know you were acquainted with him, Papa."

"Been acquainted with him for a fortnight. I sat down with him at cards last week and lost a prodigious sum."

"The two thousand pounds?"

"Oh, no, that preceded my losses to Duvane. But I do owe Duvane a considerable amount. He told me last night as we parted that he would cancel the debt and tear up my vowels if he could attend your ball. It seems a paltry favour to grant, Viola. What's one more guest?"

Especially a guest certain to enrage her husband. Viola had acquiesced earlier to Avery's demand that she not see Duvane, but she no longer would be so accommodating. Not when he was entertaining a *chère amie* at Albemarle Street.

"I will grant your request, Papa," she said.

"You will?" Mr. Challerton looked astonished. "I am most obliged to you, my dear. If there's anything I can ever do for you—"

"Just try not to sit down again to cards with Duvane," she said gently. "You will probably lose again."

"I'll do my best," he promised.

They exchanged rueful glances. "Oh, Papa, can't you find another diversion besides gaming? When you were younger, you often talked about buying back your father's estate and refurbishing it."

A sad look came over Mr. Challerton's face. "That was nothing but an air-dream, my girl. It would take considerable monies to buy it and to restore it." He shook his head. "Not that I wouldn't welcome the chance. I can remember how it looked in its glory days," he said as he pulled the carriage to a stop in front of her residence.

At last Viola was able to escape to the bedchamber and seek the comfort of her bed. But once alone, she found no relief from her thoughts.

Last night Richard had held her in his arms as they waltzed, and she had felt in utter harmony with him, enough to hope that things might come right between them. Then he had begun dressing her down about Duvane and all that time his bit of muslin waited for him at Albemarle Street.

Viola threw a pillow against the wall. The portrait of Avery's mother hanging over the bed swayed but did not fall.

Who was this *chère amie?* What did she look like? No doubt she was very beautiful, but was she astonishingly fair? Statuesque of build? Or dainty and petite? Probably blond, Viola thought morosely. They were all the rage.

She went over to her dressing table and pulled a tortoiseshell comb through her dark hair.

His unknown mistress was probably accomplished in the finer arts of the boudoir, while she was still a virgin whose husband did not appear to find her worthy of his attentions.

Viola buried her face in her hands. It was humiliating to think that after a year of marriage she and Avery had not consummated their union. And an unconsummated union was no marriage.

She lifted her head suddenly and stared at her reflection in the mirror. *No marriage. Unconsummated.* All this time the answer to her dilemma had been right under her nose. She didn't need to wait on a public bill of divorcement. She could obtain an annulment.

AFTER LEAVING Miss Garda Avery had set off for Bond Street and his usual lesson with Jackson. From there he continued on to Manton's shooting gallery where Lord Newton came upon him and requested a moment of his time.

"I have something to ask you, Richard," Newton said.

"If it's another question about Walter, I will not answer," Avery warned, taking aim at the target and shooting.

"No, it's not Walter. Or at least it only partly concerns him."

"How intriguing." Avery put down his pistol. "Well, what is it you wish to know? Is it his secret for getting the shoulders of my coats to lie perfectly flat or the trick of never getting the tassels of my hessians in a tangle?"

"No. Actually it's not Walter I wish to speak to you about. It's Miranda."

Avery took a step back. "Do you mean my cousin Miranda?"

"No, I mean Shakespeare's fairy girl," Newton ejaculated testily. "Of course I mean your cousin. Why would I even talk to you of some other Miranda?"

"My dear Hadrian, I don't even know why you are babbling to me now of my cousin. What about her?"

Lord Newton ran a finger between his neck and collar points. "Good Jupiter, what a muddle this is. Maybe I shouldn't apply to you. Just her cousin, after all. But she is enjoying your protection. I know she's of age. Lived a good number of years with that odious sister of hers, hasn't she?"

"Yes," Avery said, following this torturous recital with some difficulty. Why was Hadrian looking so redfaced? "Will you cut line and tell me what this is about?"

"Richard, don't be a gudgeon. I'm trying to tell you of my intention of making Miranda an offer."

"Of marriage?"

"Naturally, of marriage," Newton said, much affronted. "I'd hardly be talking to you if I planned to offer your relative carte blanche, would I?"

"No, most peculiar of you. And of me, that goes without saying. You've quite bowled me over. You *are* the same fellow who once told me that any married man was doomed to a long, tormented life, did you not?"

"Schoolboy ravings," Lord Newton said, straightening his cravat.

"I believe you were all of twenty-seven when you uttered them."

"I was a fool. Never thought I would take the plunge, Avery. Didn't like the idea of a leg shackle. But then I see how you and Viola go about so well."

Avery manfully refrained from venturing any opinion on his own marriage.

"Oh, I know you dashed off to the Continent in that hare-brained fashion, but since you've been back it's been smooth sailing, hasn't it?"

Avery skirted the issue. "My dear friend, you can't take the plunge just because someone else is married. You must do so because you want to. Otherwise it won't wash."

"I do want to," Newton insisted. "Miranda is just the sort of lady I'd like to marry. Not an ounce of pretension about her. She's easy and comfortable to be with, not one of these tonnish females who will always be wanting to be escorted to a soirée or assembly. She likes the country, too, and you know how partial I am to country living."

"What is it you want from me?"

"To tell me whether an offer from me would be agreeable to her."

"Good Lord, I wouldn't know that, Hadrian. I ain't blessed with second sight."

"But you could ask her, broach the topic to her. I don't wish to make an offer if she doesn't want me."

Avery gave his head an emphatic shake. "I'd just make micefeet of it. You'd best cross your Rubicon alone."

"I can't!" Lord Newton said gloomily. "If I could I would. I have tried to screw my courage to the sticking point but each time I try to get the words out they wither on my tongue. I do long to marry Miranda if it wouldn't be displeasing to her. But just think of all the fuss and botheration if she doesn't and I go there and offer for her. I'd make a cake of myself." He shuddered at the very idea.

"What a pudding-heart you are, Hadrian," Avery said with a laugh. "Is that why you have been a confirmed bachelor for so long? You've been afraid to put your fate to the touch."

"Easy for you to say," Newton bristled. "You know that females like you. I've never been much for the ladies. Females never paid a jot of attention to me."

"Well, if you are in earnest, I shall try and determine Miranda's feelings towards you. Least I can do. I wouldn't wish her to get hitched to just anyone."

"Thank you, Richard. I am obliged to you. And I know how to repay you."

Avery drew on his gloves. "You do, do you?"

"Yes. Walter has been dispatched back to Berkeley Square."

"My dear Hadrian. I'm quite overcome. But it's a trifle premature. Must I return the good Walter if Miranda does not wish to marry you?"

"No," his friend said with a laugh. "I realize that he is an excellent valet, Richard. But he is a trifle daunting. He has looked down on me ever since discovering I have moulded shoulders in my coats."

CHAPTER THIRTEEN

WALTER RETURNED to Berkeley Square, where he wrested back control of Avery's wardrobe, but not without a battle from James.

Fearing that blood would be spilled on the earl's coats, the ever-vigilant Briggs alerted Viola to the contretemps under way in Avery's private rooms. As she crossed the threshold of the dressing room, Viola's horrified eyes perceived Walter with a death grip on James's throat. Before she could stop them, James freed himself by gnawing on Walter's ear.

"Ow!" Howling, Walter fell back.

"Here now, Walter, James!" Viola intervened. "Stop this at once."

"I beg pardon, my lady," Walter said, attempting to cover his bloody ear.

"He had it coming to him," James said.

Walter did not deem this worthy of a reply and confined himself to dabbing at his ear with a handkerchief. Viola took immediate advantage of the lull in the battle to draw the other combatant off to the library.

"Now, James, that was too bad of you," she scolded. "You know that Lord Avery will always have a place for you in his employ."

"Not as a valet," James predicted.

"Were you happy as Avery's valet, James?" Viola asked gently. "It seemed to me that you were not precisely comfortable in the position, and I couldn't help thinking that you regretted volunteering for the post."

"Didn't regret it," James said, giving the globe on the earl's desk a half-hearted spin. "The work was harder than I thought it would be. I never knew his lordship's cravats could be so deuced complicated. But I would have learned if that nodcock hadn't returned."

"I'm sure you would have," she soothed. "But however much effort it took you to be a valet, you surely must realize what a superior footman you were and with practically very little effort."

"Eh, what?" Puzzlement spread on James's sturdy face.

Now that she had his attention, Viola went on swiftly. "Indeed, I'm sure that if you resumed your position here as a footman we could raise your salary."

"How large a raise?"

Still fuming at her spouse's installation of a *chère amie* at Albemarle Street, Viola did not hesitate in raising James's salary to forty pounds.

"Well, now. That's very good of you, my lady," James said, smiling broadly.

By the end of five minutes, James had been successfully coaxed out of the sulks, and freely confessed that he was a man of action, not a cork-brain who concerned himself with waistcoats and pantaloons.

"Exactly," Viola said. "And that reminds me. There is something I need delivered."

"Of course, my lady."

Viola handed the valet turned footman the invitation to Duvane that she had promised her father to send off.

"It goes to Lord Duvane at Green Street. Not a word to anyone, if you please."

"Mum's the word, my lady," James said.

After leaving the library, Viola was immediately intercepted by Miranda with news that Lord and Lady Brightly had just called with Sarah, the bosom bow Miranda had never seen before. At once, Viola made for the blue drawing room to take charge of the situation.

James, intent on his mission to deliver Lady Avery's missive to Lord Duvane and entertaining a happy vision of what he would do with the prodigious sums he would be earning as a footman, descended the Adam staircase where he found Avery just stepping across the black and white lozenges from the door.

"Ah, James, the very fellow I was hoping to see," the earl said, laying aside his multicoloured driving cape. "I must speak to you."

"Certainly, my lord."

Avery led the way into a small parlour.

"I had occasion to speak to Lord Newton, who told me that Walter would be returning to my establishment," he said, deciding to be forthright about the matter.

"Walter has already returned, my lord," James said, touching his cheek with stiff fingers. "He insisted on taking charge of your wardrobe. I protested, but he turned violent."

"Good God. No blood was spilled on my waistcoats, I hope?"

James lifted his lips in a reluctant smile. "No, my lord. But your top-boots got a trifle scuffed. I was in the midst of polishing them when Walter arrived. I believe in my anger I threw them and the shoe black at his head."

"You shock me, James. But do continue. In what condition dare I hope to find Walter?"

"Oh, he is perfectly stout, although one ear may need sewing," James confessed with a grin. "I thought it best to wait until you had returned to see if you did in fact wish Walter to take over my duties as your valet."

Avery rubbed his jaw and eyed the servant uneasily. "Well then, to be frank, James, I have appreciated your efforts, but you will agree that we haven't been entirely successful, you and I. Perhaps you might consent to spend time with Walter and have him show you a few of his secrets."

"If your lordship wishes, I will do so, but I think it a hopeless case. Walter will not share his secrets. Particularly after I bit his ear."

"You bit him? James!"

"He was choking me!"

"Ah, that makes it perfectly understandable. Perhaps I should take instruction from you instead of from Jackson." He looked across at the other man with laughter in his eyes. "If I double your salary, will that convince you to stay on as a footman?"

James inhaled a breath. Lady Avery had already increased his salary. To double it would mean he would draw eighty pounds a year. His mind boggled at such a fortune. He'd always dreamed of a pub of his own some day.

"That is good of you, my lord," he gurgled inarticulately.

Avery smiled. "What do you make now?" he enquired.

"As of ten minutes ago, my lord, I made forty pounds."

"What?" The earl's smile faded.

"Her ladyship had raised my salary, my lord. After the battle with Walter."

"Oh, she did, did she?" Avery said, momentarily nettled, then his ready sense of the ridiculous saved the day. "Well, that's beaten me all to hollow, but it's a stroke of fortune for you. I am a man of my word. I offered to double your salary. And since it stood as of ten minutes ago at forty pounds, that means you will draw eighty pounds a year if you stay on as my footman. You will undoubtedly be the best paid footman in all London."

Flushed with this windfall, James fanned himself distractedly with the invitation in his hand.

"Far better to be the best paid footman than the worst valet in London," he admitted.

"You will get no argument there from me," the earl said, his eyes narrowing as he noticed the note in the servant's hand. Only minutes ago, James had been his valet. Who would be giving him messages to deliver as a footman except Viola?

What was she sending off? And to whom? By cocking his head to the left and squinting he was able to discern the name of her correspondent. *Duvane.*

His wife was dispatching *billets-doux* to her lover. With a Herculean effort Avery restrained himself from snatching the missive from James and hurling it into the fire. *Devil take it!* Here was more evidence that she nursed a tendre for Duvane.

"Will you be needing me for anything else, my lord?" James asked.

"No, James. I daresay you have an urgent errand to run for her ladyship, have you not?"

The footman's startled expression confirmed Avery's suspicions. The earl turned on his heel and walked out of the parlour. Where the devil was Viola?

His search took him through one room after another before he heard voices and the sound of laughter trailing out from the blue drawing room.

Unnoticed, he stood in the doorway for a moment, watching Miranda and Viola tending to their guests. Viola resembled a nymph in a day dress of sea-water green, her face alight with animation. When she turned and saw him, her smile froze. She started to rise.

"I beg pardon, my dear, I had no notion you were entertaining guests," he drawled, coming forward.

"Avery, allow me to present Lord and Lady Brightly."

"Oh, Lord Avery, such a pleasure," Lady Brightly trilled. Her high-pitched voice raised Avery's hackles immediately. "I was just telling Lady Avery what a joy it would be to meet you at last. And here you are."

"Yes," he said and exchanged a bow with Brightly, a stout fellow with a bristling moustache.

"I had hoped to meet you before next week's ball," Lady Brightly went on.

He turned an incredulous eye on Viola. He had left the matter of the guest list in her hands, but surely she had not invited the Brightlys?

"Balls have never been much in our way of things," Lord Brightly said now.

"But they will be next Season when we bring Maggie out," his wife reminded her spouse tartly. "Maggie is our daughter—" she turned to Avery "—and we are hoping to make a brilliant match for her."

"My congratulations," he said. Such plain speaking in front of strangers was bad ton. What on earth did Viola mean by inviting them to the ball?

"And this is Sarah Hawkins," Viola said, bringing Sarah forward. "She and Miranda are bosom bows."

Avery's smile was less forced as he directed it towards Sarah. "Miss Hawkins."

"Sarah is our governess," Lady Brightly tittered. "We are quite fond of her. She's almost one of the family."

Sarah blushed, as well she might with a family like the Brightlys, Avery thought.

"It appears to me that I've heard the name Brightly before," he said to Lord Brightly. "Perhaps at the club?"

"I don't belong to any club," the other man answered.

"Perhaps if you spoke for him, Lord Avery—"

Avery blinked, and even Viola looked aghast. To ask such a favour at first meeting! What would the woman ask at a second meeting?

"Obliged to you, but I don't want membership in any club," Lord Brightly said stoutly. "All the gentlemen do there is play cards for prodigiously high stakes."

"We occasionally read a newspaper or journal," Avery said. His words jogged his recalcitrant memory. "That's where I read your name. In the newspaper, wasn't it?"

"Bound to be there," Brightly acknowledged. "We were robbed."

"Lost my best jewels," Lady Brightly said, her face turning bright pink at the memory. "The thieves knew exactly where I kept them."

"How unfortunate. Has any progress been made in apprehending the culprits?"

"None."

"I heard that a reward was being offered by the various victims. Shall you be joining that offer?" Viola asked.

Lord Brightly looked alarmed. "Don't know. Haven't been approached."

The earl correctly comprehended that Brightly was disinclined to contribute to the reward.

"We're not the only ones who have been robbed," Lady Brightly interjected. "It's cold comfort, but we have plenty of company. The Havershams were robbed last night."

"That's Miss Dawson's household," Sarah whispered to Viola.

"An accomplished governess, Miss Dawson," Lady Brightly said, overhearing. "She plays the pianoforte. Dear Sarah does not. Do you play, Miss Symes?"

"Why, yes, I do."

Owing to Viola's expert manoeuvrings, they soon adjourned to the music room where Miranda and Lady Brightly began playing a series of duets. The earl's best Madeira was unearthed by Viola who in an urgent aside beseeched her husband to remember his duties as a host with regard to Lord Brightly.

Viola herself went over to the small settee to speak to Sarah, determined to learn all she could about the latest robbery. Under the cover of the thunderous piano, Viola enquired about Miss Dawson's state of mind.

"I don't know. I haven't seen her yet. But I suspect the Runners questioned her just as vigorously as they did me.'' She shivered at the memory. ''How I wish these dreadful crimes would cease. Most of my friends have been employed in the households which have been robbed.''

''They have?'' Viola asked, surprised by this revelation.

''I don't understand it,'' Sarah went on. ''How do the robbers know exactly where the jewels are kept? It's uncanny.''

''I don't know. But I assure you I shall get to the bottom of this.''

The governess smiled. ''What can you do?''

''Something. Anything,'' Viola said decisively. ''Are things better for you now than before?''

''Oh, yes.'' Sarah's smile broadened. ''It is infamous to confess, but being your friend has improved my lot considerably. Though I suspect that Lord Avery does not fully approve of Lord Brightly.''

Miss Hawkins was right on the mark in this assessment. The earl had stigmatized Brightly as the worst mushroom he'd ever met.

''Are you foxed? To even dream of inviting those people to the ball?'' he expostulated after they had gone and he was alone with Viola in the drawing room. ''Toad-eaters.''

''That's doing it too brown,'' she retorted. ''He is a trifle prosy, perhaps—''

''The dullest dog in Christendom.''

''He seemed most appreciative of your Madeira.''

"Drank it down as though it were water," Avery said with a snort. "That shows how little he knows about good wine. Next time they call, pray give me fair warning so I can absent myself."

"I don't think they will make a habit of calling," Viola said. "But Miranda and Sarah are friends, so it seemed innocent enough to invite Sarah and her employers to the ball."

"You were talking to Sarah more than Miranda was," he pointed out.

"Only because Miranda was obliged to play the piano," Viola answered easily. "Sarah is a very amiable young woman."

"Didn't say anything against Sarah. She at least conducted herself like a sensible woman."

Viola stiffened. No doubt a sensible woman would take the installation of her husband's mistress as the merest trifle. Why had she ever hoped that he would love her. The sooner she ended this marriage, the better.

The earl, for his part, was wondering if he had been too harsh in his denunciation of the Brightlys. A mushroom married to a cursed bagpipe, but the earl had tolerated worse.

"Let's forget about the Brightlys," he said now. "I have something I wish to discuss with you. It concerns Miranda."

"Miranda?" Viola was astonished. Heretofore Avery had not bothered himself with Miranda's affairs.

"Yes, I daresay it will please you that she needn't be forced to marry that odious farmer in Devonshire if she doesn't wish to. I have received a flattering offer for her."

"Really? Don't keep me on tenterhooks," she protested. "Who is it from?"

He could not help smiling at her eagerness. "Hadrian."

She looked blank for a moment. "Do you mean Lord Newton?"

"I do. He is very much taken with her. I should have seen it from the first. Today at Manton's he demanded to know what feelings she has for him. He hesitates to put his fate to the touch without assurance of acceptance. And since you know more about Miranda's feelings on marriage, I put the matter to you."

"To me? He would do better to talk to Miranda himself."

"I told him that, but he turned tail at the mere idea. He asked me to do it. But I'd just make micefeet of it. Would you talk to Miranda? Newton is in earnest about his feelings for her."

"I don't know," she said, taken aback by the request.

"What think you of such a match?" he asked, curious about her opinion.

She frowned, thinking hard for a few moments. "I would say it has as much a chance of success as any other arrangement. And probably more than some, including our own." She dared not look in his eyes.

Avery twisted his lips wryly. "Will you oblige me by speaking to Miranda?"

Viola still hesitated. "You do not know the pressure females feel when presented with an offer from a gentleman," she murmured.

"Did you feel such pressure?" he asked. Had Challerton bullocked her into accepting his offer?

"I know of what I speak," she said. "And I am loath to inflict a similar pressure on Miranda."

"If she doesn't want him, all she need do is say no. What kind of ogre do you think I am, Viola!" he exclaimed, raking his fingers through his hair. "I would never force Miranda into an unhappy alliance."

"Like ours?"

"Were you forced into marrying me?" he demanded.

"No," she admitted. "I wanted the match."

Wanted my money, the earl reminded himself.

"What about Miranda?" he asked briskly, not about to be led off on a tangent. "I did promise Hadrian to see how the land lies."

"Since you both fight shy of speaking to her, I shall do it," she agreed. "I warn you, if she is not disposed to find Newton pleasing I won't say she is."

"I wouldn't want you to lie."

She prepared to leave the room to speak to Miranda directly, but he laid a hand on her arm.

"Another moment of your time, my dear. I understand you gave James a raise if he stayed on as footman here."

"Don't you think he deserved it?" she asked, trembling from the sudden contact of his fingers on her bare skin. "He was quite shocked at the way Walter took command of your dressing room without warning. Under the circumstances, I thought a raise in salary was well deserved. James is a good footman when he's not trying to be a valet."

"He'd better be a superior footman, because he'll be the best paid one in Town," he said with a quizzing look at her.

Viola lifted a sceptical brow. "Hardly that. I raised his salary ten pounds. That puts him at forty pounds for the year. A goodly sum, I grant you, but not the best paid. I believe Dorothea pays one of her footmen fifty pounds a year."

"What you don't know is I offered to double James's salary before I knew that you had already raised it to forty pounds."

Her eyes widened. "Richard, that means—"

"James will be drawing eighty pounds a year," he finished for her. "He'll be making more than Briggs!"

"Good heavens. Do you think Briggs will find out?"

"There is not a doubt about that. The news has probably already spread in the servants' quarters. That means that we shall probably have to give Briggs a raise, too. And quite possibly the other footmen and the maids, and don't forget Henri. As the chef, he is accustomed to commanding the largest salary of all."

"Will we be reduced to penury, sir?" she asked, unable to help smiling at the idea of all the servants standing in line outside the earl's door.

"I hope not. If worse comes to worst, we can sack the lot of them and hire a new crop from an employment service."

The amusement in her eyes died abruptly at the mention of employment service.

"What's the matter?" he asked at once.

"Nothing." She didn't want to think of employment services, particularly the one which staffed his house on Albemarle Street.

"Don't lie to me. Tell me," he commanded. He gave her shoulders a shake.

She gazed mutely up into his blue eyes. Should she ask him who he had installed as his mistress in Albemarle Street? She wanted to, but she dared not. To ask such a question would be to bring out once and for all how inadequate a partner he found her.

"I'd best go and speak to Miranda about Lord Newton," she said, and fled the room.

CHAPTER FOURTEEN

PETER THACKER LEANED back in the Etruscan-armed chair and smiled across the parlour as Miss Garda bent her dark head over the first page of Miss Austen's novel.

"'It is a truth universally accepted, that a single man with a large fortune must be in want of a wife,'" she read laboriously before turning her brown eyes on him.

"Oh, I say, that's famous!" Thacker clapped his hands.

"Famous? You mean it is of renown?"

He shook his head. "No, well, yes. 'Famous' does mean 'of renown.' But I just meant that your reading was on the mark."

"On what mark?" Miss Garda asked, turning the book over and examining its cover.

Mr. Thacker gave his head another shake. "No, that's just an expression we English use. Nothing to get in the hips about."

"Hips?" Miss Garda put one hand to her hip in confusion. "I do not understand you, Mr. Thacker."

"No, of course you don't," Mr. Thacker said, rubbing his chin. "I just meant that you were reading very well."

Her eyes lit up. "Then why did you not say so?" she asked.

He chuckled. "I thought I had. I beg pardon. I'm such a poor hand at teaching anyone English. But you won't have to suffer through my schooling much longer. I've engaged a tutor for you who will teach you how to go on."

"How to go on where?" Miss Garda asked. "I know, that is just another of your English impressions, correct?"

"English expressions," he corrected gently.

She laughed along with him. "Do you know, Mr. Thacker, I think that while I can read English, I may not be able to speak it the way you do here in London."

"Of course you will. It takes time, that's all. Keep reading, why don't you?"

Encouraged, Miss Garda finished the page, acquitting herself so well in this assignment that Mr. Thacker called a halt to the day's lesson.

"Good!" she exclaimed, putting down the novel at once. "I have a great wish to see London. Do you think I might go out of this house for a while?"

"Well, I don't know." Mr. Thacker gazed into the smiling eyes of Miss Garda. He felt as though he were embarking on a perilous path. Miss Garda, he reminded himself, was the earl's "friend."

"You do have a carriage?" she asked.

"Er, yes."

"I would very much like some fresh air," she said, looking so hopeful that he was struck to the core.

"Then fresh air you shall have," Mr. Thacker said recklessly.

Five minutes later, Miss Garda was seated next to him in his vehicle, gazing raptly at all the sights.

"That's Parliament," he said, pointing out the building as they passed. "Lord Avery speaks there on occasion."

"Does he? An intelligent man."

"Oh, the earl's brain is second to none," Thacker agreed.

"He visited me this morning."

"Did he?" Mr. Thacker was well acquainted with the earl's habits. Avery rarely bestirred himself before noon. "I trust he was pleased with the arrangements?"

"Oh, yes." Miss Garda's head bobbed up and down. "Lord Avery is very kind."

Mr. Thacker bit his lip. Kind? The earl's set-downs were legendary.

"To his favourites he is kind," he replied finally. And Miss Garda, Thacker reminded himself, was definitely one of Avery's favourites.

"Is he married?" she asked after a moment.

"Yes," Mr. Thacker said as they took the turn towards the Strand.

"What is his wife like?"

"Quite beautiful and kind."

"Like him. How happy they must be together," Miss Garda said with a thoughtful expression on her dark face.

OVER AT BERKELEY SQUARE, the beautiful and kind Lady Avery was determined neither to pressure nor to frighten Miranda with Newton's offer. However, she was curious to discover what feelings, if any, Miranda had for Avery's boon companion. She found the perfect opportunity for a tête-à-tête that afternoon when Miranda came upon her arranging gladiolas and volunteered to help.

"I often did arrangements at home," she said.

"Do you miss the country?" Viola asked, wiping her hands on a cloth and watching Miranda's deft fingers insert the long-stemmed flowers into the blue-and-white porcelain vase.

"I suppose so. I do prefer the country to the city. Although everyone here has been so nice to me."

"Have you perchance thought much of that squire you left behind?"

Miranda turned so suddenly that her elbow collided with the vase. It tottered for a moment before Viola caught it and placed it back on the table.

"Viola, don't tell me that odious Mr. Leonard is coming to visit London," Miranda responded. "I vow, I couldn't bear it. Yolanda would not send him to London after me, would she? Even she cannot be so cruel."

Alarmed at Miranda's reaction to her bumbling question, Viola quickly calmed her fears.

"He is not coming to London. I just wondered if perchance you were missing him and his offer of marriage."

"No!" Miranda said with such violence that there could be no doubt as to her feelings for the squire.

She separated another long-stemmed flower from the bunch.

"Indeed, the more I think of him the worse he seems, particularly now that I have met the gentlemen here in London."

"Ah, you approve of someone in particular?"

"They are all very amiable."

"You don't have a preference?"

Miranda frowned, but it was the flower arrangement that offended her sensibility and not Viola's question.

"Lord Keynes is perhaps the best dancer," she said, hastily rearranging a flower. "And Captain Lovejoy and Major Lacey are ever so dashing. Did you see them at Lady Sefton's ball in their regimentals?"

Viola nodded. "I have often thought that gentlemen should be forbidden to wear regimentals at balls," she said.

Miranda laughed in agreement. "I suppose of them all Mr. Lucas is the most fashionable, don't you think?"

"A veritable tulip."

Miranda continued in this lively vein, naming several other gentlemen whose company she enjoyed. When she failed to mention Newton, Viola finally broached his name herself.

"What of Lord Newton?"

Miranda smiled. "Oh, he is quite a pet. Like the older brother I always wished I had. He is so civil and patient, fetching me a glass of champagne and telling me droll stories about cousin Richard. Is it true that he once swallowed a tadpole on a dare?"

"Good heavens, I hope not!" Viola exclaimed. "Although if anyone would know about such things it would be Hadrian."

Miranda laughed. "He's the best of good fellows."

"I am glad to hear that you are such friends," Viola said.

"Yes," Miranda said with a happy nod but with no sign of grand passion. "It was so decent of him to return Walter. And did you really raise James's salary to eighty pounds?"

"Oh pray, and how did you hear of it?"

"The story is all over the house."

"Actually I just raised it to forty pounds. Avery raised it to eighty pounds," Viola said distractedly, not wanting to be led off into a discussion of her servant's wages. "Miranda, what if I told you that Avery mentioned Newton was looking for a wife."

Miranda's eyes widened. "Really? I wonder that Newton did not speak to me himself!"

"That's exactly what I told Avery," Viola said, studying Miranda's eager expression. "So you don't dislike the idea?"

"Not at all. I shall comb his hair for it when next we meet. How could he keep this news from me? I would have been only too happy to help him in the hunt for a suitable wife. We don't want him marrying a hurly-burly female. What sort of wife does he want? I suppose he has a list of requirements?" She said, coming to the end of her litany of questions. "Some gentlemen are very particular."

"Miranda, are you willing to find Newton a wife?" Viola asked.

"Of course. What else are friends for?"

"Have you ever thought that perhaps you might be a suitable wife for him?" she suggested gently.

Miranda's laughter bubbled up. "Me? That's absurd."

"He is quite an eligible *parti.*"

"I know that, so we shan't have any trouble at all finding a wife for him. I'm surprised that he has not applied himself to the task before this Season. I have heard that he was nearly as opposed to the marital state as Avery," she confided. "And he has a title, which some females think so important."

"You don't think a title is important?"

"Not terribly. I'd as lief have an untitled man as a titled man I did not like, wouldn't you?"

"Yes, of course. But can you divulge just what would be important for you when it comes to marrying a gentleman," Viola asked curiously, "if titles are not?"

Miranda dusted her hands, the flowers at last arranged to her satisfaction.

"You will laugh."

"Indeed, I will not," Viola promised.

Miranda paused, obviously collecting her thoughts. "I want a gentleman who will set my pulses racing," she confessed finally. "You will undoubtedly tell me I have been reading too many circulating-library romances, but isn't it true that when in love your heart pounds and you feel breathless and close to swooning?"

"Sometimes," Viola said, looking away from Miranda's intent face. It reminded her too much of herself a year ago when she was top over tail in love with Avery.

"Is that how Richard makes you feel?" Miranda asked earnestly.

"Sometimes," came Viola's quiet reply.

"Was he very angry with you today because of the Brightlys?"

"Well, he did not precisely like them and thought it very foolish of me to have become acquainted with them, but he seemed to think that Sarah was a sensible young woman."

"As do I. She is the sweetest creature, and if we were not bosom bows before we soon shall be."

VIOLA LOST NO TIME in finding Avery in his library and alerting him to Miranda's feelings for Hadrian.

"She thinks him amiability itself but fell into whoops at the suggestion of marrying him."

The earl, seated behind his mahogany desk, shook his head in disgust. "What a silly widgeon. I hope you told her what a henwit she was. A better man than Hadrian would be hard for any lady to find."

"Indeed, I did no such thing," she retorted. "It was not my place to further Newton's suit, but merely to determine what Miranda's feelings for him were. I have done so. She considers him the older brother she never had."

"That isn't what Newton wants to hear."

"Perhaps you could speak to Miranda. Your facility of address no doubt surpasses mine."

Avery drummed his fingers lightly on the desk, ignoring her last remark.

"Perhaps I should have applied to Susan for help. There's nothing she finds more refreshing than plotting marriage for unsuspecting souls. Are you sure you didn't say something to set Miranda's back against marriage."

"Such as what, pray?" she asked.

Avery shrugged. "Perhaps in conversation with her you might have hinted about your own unhappiness in marriage and thus tainted her view of the institution."

Viola could not believe her ears. "How little you know me, sir, if you think that I would play such a shabby trick on Miranda and alleviate my wretched unhappiness at her expense.'' She nearly choked on the words. ''Nonetheless you are right to notice that I am unhappy in this marriage.''

To her intense mortification tears welled up in her eyes.

Avery pushed back his chair and started towards her, but it was too late. She had already fled.

Feeling annoyed with her and with himself, the earl returned to his work, but he could not concentrate on the papers laid out in front of him.

He slammed a fist down on his desk. He should never have returned to London! Things certainly had not turned out the way he had envisioned. Try as he might, he couldn't get over having seen tears in Viola's eyes. Confound it! Probably just another one of her tricks. He'd meant no offence by his words. He'd been thinking only of Miranda's future. He would not be treated like a tyrant. By Jupiter, she would listen to him.

He stormed out of the library and was half-way down the corridor when he heard the sound of a flute coming from the music room. Blood drained from his face. She was playing that damn composition again, the one she'd written for Duvane. The earl stood as though rooted in the hallway, feeling every note ripping into his heart. Fool! She hadn't loved him from the start, and she certainly didn't now. She loved that coxcomb, Duvane. He had only to listen to the music and remember the *billet-doux* she'd send off with James to be sure of it.

Just then Briggs came down the opposite end of the hallway. He had a good deal to tell his lordship about the exorbitant sum paid to a mere footman in his establishment, but as the butler drew closer to the earl, he suffered a quick change of mind. His lordship wore the look of one about to do murder.

"Briggs, inform Henri that I dine at White's tonight," Avery said.

"Yes, my lord." This was definitely not the occasion to bring up his salary with his employer.

As AVERY STEPPED into the dining room at White's, the last person in London he wished to see intercepted him.

Newton.

"Did you ask Miranda?" Hadrian demanded, taking his fences in a rush as they walked to a table.

"No, Viola did," Avery replied as a waiter approached with the menus.

Newton waved the fellow off. "Speak, Richard," he demanded.

"Not until I place my order for dinner," Avery said, summoning the waiter and ordering rack of lamb for two. "I'm deuced hungry."

"*Now* will you tell me what Miranda said?" Newton complained.

"Calm yourself, my friend, or you will have an apoplexy. Miranda is very fond of you, but rather like an older brother."

A look of acute disgust spread across Newton's ruddy face.

"What? A brother!" he exclaimed. "Of all the nonsensical notions. You must be bamming me."

"It could be worse. She might be thinking of you as a father."

"She would not dare," Newton muttered. "A brother. Good Jupiter, what a come-down."

"Plenty of other fish in the sea."

"I don't want another fish." Newton stared fixedly at the table of gleaming silver. "I want Miranda."

"You do?" Avery was surprised at this change in his friend. "Scarcely hours ago you fought shy at even asking her to marry you."

"Yes, I know. But that's because I thought you could make a better job of it. I might have got swept away with my feelings and I didn't wish to frighten such a gently reared creature. But you've been no help at all, Richard," he chided. "Indeed, you made a muddle of things."

"I beg pardon. It was inadvertent," the earl said, feeling much harassed. "Perhaps the next time a friend calls upon me to offer marriage to a female on his behalf I shall do better."

"I should hope so," Hadrian replied. "I could have made my own offer if I'd known this would be the result."

"You should have," Avery retorted.

Fortunately, the food arrived just then, diverting them both. Avery ate heartily. Newton, however, merely picked at the tender bits of lamb drenched in morel sauce.

"I suppose Miranda has many sprigs dangling after her?" he asked gloomily.

"I haven't kept count of her callers. Why?" Avery wiped his mouth with a napkin. "What scheme are you hatching?"

"Just my courtship. A most unbrotherly one."

Avery took a long swallow of wine. "You realize she's my cousin and enjoys my protection in London," he murmured.

"Your fears are needless," Hadrian said. "I am a gentleman and am not about to seduce her!"

"Much obliged to you."

"If I did, you would have to call me out. Sticky business duelling with your best friend."

"Yes, I might be obliged to shoot you," Avery said with undiminished affability. "What do you have in mind?"

"I'm going to wage a campaign for her hand," Hadrian said, with a gleam in his eye. "I vow she won't think of me as a brother after the week is out."

WHILE NEWTON launched his own plan to win the hand of the fair Miranda, Viscount Duvane was sitting down to cards in his favourite Greeking establishment, feeling quite pleased with himself, a consequence of having received Viola's invitation to her ball.

How furious Avery would be, and there was nothing he could do about it. To order an invited guest to leave would be bad ton, sure to cause scandal.

Duvane chuckled happily to himself at the imagined scene and spread his cards out on the table. The winning hand yet again. He scooped up the money in the middle of the table. His luck was taking a definite turn for the better.

To help his luck along, he had recourse to use the ace hidden in his sleeve before the night was over, and when Mr. Challerton sought him out at midnight Duvane stood five hundred pounds to the good and was quite willing to quit the table.

"Never knew you to quit before when the luck was running your way," young Mr. Talbot said suspiciously.

"There is always a first time," Duvane said urbanely. "Come Challerton, the air here is getting oppressive. Let's talk outside."

Mr. Challerton stepped out into the street with Duvane. A passing job-chaise clattered by, the only sound in the deserted street.

"This won't take long," he said. "I talked to my daughter on your behalf. She said she'd dispatch an invitation to you to her ball forthwith."

"What an excellent daughter you have," Duvane said. He inhaled deeply of the night air, feeling in an expansive mood. "I have already received the invitation."

"Good. That cancels the matter of my gambling debts, then."

"Of course. I am a man of my word."

"Not that I doubt your word," Challerton said sceptically, "but I'd like my vowels back."

"Don't you trust me?"

A crafty look came over Challerton's face. "I watched you tonight when you played your cards. You took the ace from your left sleeve. A trifle ham-handed, my lord. You'd do better not to try it from the left next time."

"Are you calling me a cheat?" Duvane said coldly.

"It's nothing to me how you play with other men," Challerton said. "I lost to you, and I'm not quarrelling whether the losses were legitimate or not. But I want my markers back."

"Do you think I carry them with me, fool?"

"I shall see you to your home, my lord."

Duvane glared, but he allowed Viola's father to accompany him to Green Street. While Challerton waited in the parlour, the viscount went to his library safe. A few minutes later, he tossed the bundle of vowels into Challerton's lap.

"Will you count them?"

"I think I shall," Challerton said, "just to be certain." He licked his thumb and began doing so.

Duvane poured himself a brandy and watched in amused silence. Finally Challerton nodded.

"Our business is at an end, my lord."

"Stay and have a glass of brandy," Duvane said, handing one to him. "How did you know I was cheating tonight?"

Challerton sipped the brandy. "I haven't been sitting down at cards all these years without learning something about the Captain Sharps."

"Maybe you'd do well to put that knowledge to work yourself."

Challerton shook his head. "Not me. I don't have the bottom to be a cheat."

Duvane inclined his head slightly, taking this rebuke for a compliment.

"I'm obliged to you for the invitation to your daughter's ball. I hope it doesn't cause any awkwardness between Avery and her the night of the ball."

Challerton shrugged. "It doesn't matter if it does. Viola tells me a divorce is in her future. Your appearance at the ball probably won't set well in Richard's dish, but it won't do any more harm to the marriage than has already been done by the two of them," he said sagely.

"What do you mean, divorce?" Duvane demanded. It wouldn't be any revenge to cause mischief if the marriage was already at an end. "You must be mistaken. She wouldn't dare seek a bill of divorcement."

"You don't know my daughter very well, do you?" Challerton enquired drily.

CHAPTER FIFTEEN

VIOLA SAT in her sitting room, furiously jabbing a needle into her tambour and wishing it were Avery's heart. She would not remain married to that man. She would not. She would go to work in a mill first. She would emigrate. She would find those burglars and claim the reward.

Much preferring this last idea to her two previous, she reviewed her conversation with Sarah about Miss Dawson's employers, the Havershams.

Poor Miss Dawson had been obliged to go through an interrogation by the Runners, just as Sarah had. So had the Morelys' governess. Viola frowned and put down her embroidery.

Was it sheer coincidence that the burglars struck a number of houses where Sarah's friends were employed? Or could it have been deliberate?

But that was absurd. How would the thieves know about Sarah and the other governesses? Sarah couldn't be acquainted with any ruffians, and certainly Miss Dawson would give them short shrift. Burglars did not congregate where governesses did.

Congregate. Viola stared up at a cherub adorning her ceiling. The governesses frequented the Rose Garden tea room at Piccadilly. And so too did a certain Zorah, the Gypsy woman.

That was the answer. It had to be.

And yet Sarah and Miss Dawson had stated emphatically that the Gypsy woman had done nothing untoward during their private reading, merely supplying reassuring answers to their questions.

All Viola's thinking was giving her the headache. She pressed her fingertips to her temples. There was only one way to learn what she need to about Zorah. She would lay a trap for the Gypsy woman tomorrow.

Just as she finished making up her mind about this, Miranda knocked on her door.

"Viola, are you hungry?" she asked as she stepped into the sitting room. "I vow I am famished."

"I daresay I could use a little nourishment," Viola acknowledged with a smile, her appetite and good humour restored by her plans for the morrow. "We needn't change for dinner. It will be just the two of us this evening."

"Where is cousin Avery?" Miranda asked, following her out of the room and down the stairs.

"Dining at his club. Briggs informed me."

"Does he do so often?"

"Now and then," Viola said lightly, dismissing the question as best she could. But even as she linked her arm through Miranda's she could not help wondering if Avery would really dine this evening at White's or would he seek the culinary comforts to be found with his doxy at Albemarle Street.

DUE TO HEAVY PLAY at the green baize tables Avery's return to Berkeley Square coincided with the mantel clock chiming the hour of three. He left strict orders not to be disturbed before noon. Walter, now firmly ensconced as his lordship's valet, was determined to carry out his master's wishes.

There was no necessity for Walter to be concerned with her ladyship. Viola had spent most of the night trying to think of an excuse to slip away unnoticed to the tea room. Now, with Avery closeted until noon, the perfect opportunity loomed.

Garbed once again in Polly's brown dress, Viola was crossing the black and white lozenges towards the door just as Miranda turned the corner from the hallway.

"Viola? Is that you? Where are you going dressed like that?" she exclaimed.

Viola halted, feverishly trying to think of a suitable explanation for her dowdy rig.

"Miranda, do keep your voice down, my dear," she urged. "Richard is still abed. I am on my way to a rehearsal at Lady Dixon's."

"But Lady Dixon told me she was bound for a drive to Hampton Court this morning," Miranda protested.

Viola was at point non plus. How vexatious of Dorothea to have discussed her plans with Miranda.

"I know you are my hostess and have more rank than I could dream of," Miranda said hesitantly, "but I am your senior by two years. I feel compelled to ask you just what you are doing."

Viola saw no other recourse but the truth. "I've had a sudden notion who might be masterminding the robberies here in London."

"Do you mean the break-ins?" Miranda asked eagerly.

Viola nodded. "I am disguised, you see. Avery would never approve of my trying to solve these crimes. That's why I must do what I can before he rises."

"May I go with you?" Miranda asked as Viola moved towards the door again.

"You? Certainly not."

Usually the most compliant of guests, Miranda now turned mulish, vowing to follow her anyway and thus make micefeet of her plans.

Viola eyed the recalcitrant face warily. "Very well, come along. But first change from that walking dress into something old and fusty."

Fifteen minutes later, wearing a suitably old and fusty green dress, Miranda climbed into the hack that Viola hailed. Once the carriage was rolling over the cobblestone street, Viola revealed her full suspicions about the Gypsy tea room to Miranda who, far from being fearful, thought it a great lark.

"Nothing like this happens in dull old Devonshire," she declared.

"It may be dangerous," Viola warned, wondering if she had been right to bring Miranda along. Avery would doubtless ring a peal over her. "Whatever happens you must not look in the crystal ball. I suspect that the Gypsy mesmerizes people by asking them to gaze into it.''

"I know all about Gypsies," Miranda said with an authoritative air.

"Do you? How came you by your knowledge?" Viola asked, wincing as the carriage swayed to avoid a dip in the road.

"There was a band of Gypsies which used to travel every summer to our village," Miranda explained, hanging on for dear life, as well. "Crystal balls are the least of what they carry in their wagons. I think we should avoid looking in her eyes or at any locket she may begin to swing in front of us."

"An excellent suggestion," Viola said. "We must also pretend to be asleep and fall under the spell so we can answer the questions she is sure to ask about where we keep the jewels in our household."

"You're not going to tell her the truth!" Miranda exclaimed.

"No. I will tell her that my employer keeps her cache of jewels in her bedchamber on the second floor in the east wing. Behind the picture of a female ancestor over her bed."

"But you've just described your bedchamber, Viola."

"Yes, I know. I'll also tell the Gypsy that my lady will be attending a musicale tonight."

"Tonight? So soon?" Miranda asked, her initial enthusiasm somewhat dampened.

"I'm replying on their greed to tempt the Gypsy and her cronies to make an attempt tonight. When they do, I shall capture them." She shot a quick look at Miranda. "There is a reward for their capture. You deserve half of it."

"Oh, heavens, no!" Miranda rejected this generous offer. "You have done all the planning and the thinking. The reward most assuredly belongs to you."

The vehicle stopped in Piccadilly in front of the tea room.

"Now do remember our plan," Viola said, preparing to leave the carriage. "And don't look into the crystal ball."

The Rose Garden was deserted save for a pair of women conversing over a pot of Bohea at a table near the door. Viola sat down but made no pretence of ordering tea, asking immediately for Zorah.

"I have great need of her," she said, wringing a lace-trimmed handkerchief in her hands.

"Why are you looking so agitated, Viola?" Miranda demanded as the waitress went off.

"So the Gypsy will give me a reading. Hush, here she comes."

Zorah, the Gypsy, strolled out from the back room. She wore a black skirt with a red low-cut blouse and a shawl over her shoulders.

"Miss asked for me?" she enquired, her hooped earrings swaying ever so slightly.

Was it possible to be mesmerized by the earrings, Viola wondered, steadfastly avoiding them.

"Yes. I have desperate need of a private reading."

The Gypsy smiled, showing sharp white teeth.

"A private reading will cost two pounds."

Viola tossed the coins on the table. The Gypsy snatched them up.

"Follow me," she said.

Viola rose along with Miranda. The Gypsy frowned and shook her head.

"If she comes it will be another two pounds."

"But she doesn't want a reading," Viola said.

Zorah sniffed. "Even so, if she comes into the back it will be an extra two pounds."

"Outrageous. I'll give you one," Viola said.

At first the Gypsy seemed tempted to argue, then nodded her agreement. Viola handed over the additional pound and with no further obstacle the three women went through the small doorway into a small dimly lit room.

Dust motes swam in the light of a single window. In the middle of the room, a round table had been set up with the much-mentioned crystal ball. The gypsy threw off her shawl. A gold locket hung from her neck. Miranda shot Viola a warning look. Viola did her best not to look at the locket.

"Now then, Miss..."

"Brown. Violet Brown," Viola said.

"Now then, Miss Brown, be seated and tell me what troubles you."

Viola took the chair indicated and Miranda the one next to it. "It's the man I love. I'm not sure if he loves me."

"Let us see what the crystal ball says."

The Gypsy waved her hands over the crystal ball, muttered an incantation that Viola could not fully comprehend and then began to speak.

"I see another woman with him. Not you. She smiles and he smiles. She laughs, and he laughs. He is quite taken with her."

"What do you see happening to her?"

"I see a grand house. Servants. He is with her."

Viola bit her lip. Even though this was just a story the Gypsy concocted to beguile her victims, it was close enough to the truth about Avery that Viola felt uneasy.

"Where is the house?" Miranda asked.

The Gypsy frowned. "That is not clear. Perhaps if miss looks into the crystal ball she can see it."

Viola inhaled a breath and glanced at Miranda. The fateful moment loomed. Viola took a quick peek at the ball, seeing nothing but a cloudy crystal and drew her head back.

"I didn't see anything."

"Perhaps you didn't look long enough."

"I am not the one with the gift of prophecy," Viola said tartly. "I thought you were. That's why I came to you."

Zorah shrugged. "There are other methods besides the crystal ball. Give me your hand."

Reluctantly Viola held it out.

"A long life line—that's very good. And a long heart line. But you see how it curves here. That means that there will be heartbreak for you." Viola's hand trembled. The Gypsy noticed.

"You are so nervous, miss. Calm yourself. Your emanations are most confusing. Perhaps you can calm yourself by looking at my locket. I will let it swing back and forth, and you will be able to relax."

"How pleasant," Viola said, glancing over at Miranda, who gave her an encouraging nod.

The gold heart-shaped locket swung back and forth in front of Viola's face. Viola narrowed her eyes to keep from looking at it, a ploy the Gypsy interpreted as succumbing to the spell, judging by the triumphant look in the dark eyes.

"You are feeling very comfortable. Very relaxed," the Gypsy suggested. "In fact so comfortable you can scarcely keep your eyes open."

Viola allowed them to close. She let her breathing deepen, hoping that would convince the woman she was asleep.

"And you are feeling comfortable and relaxed, too," the Gypsy said.

"Comfortable and relaxed," Miranda replied.

Viola felt a frisson of fear. Miranda sounded entirely too comfortable and relaxed.

"Sleep, the two of you. Fall into a deep sleep."

Viola felt her chest rising and falling. She heard Miranda's rhythmic breathing next to her. She only prayed that Miranda was pretending, as she was.

"Who do you work for?" Zorah's voice was now brisk and clear.

"Lady Avery," Viola said.

"Where does she live?"

"Berkeley Square, Number 12," Miranda replied before Viola could do so.

"Where does your employer keep her jewels?"

"In her bedchamber on the second floor in the east wing," Viola answered.

"Where in the bedchamber?"

"In her safe."

"And where is the safe?"

"Behind the painting."

"Which painting?!" The Gypsy sounded exasperated.

"The one over her bed."

"The safe is behind this painting?"

"Yes."

"Very good. What kind of jewels does she keep there?"

"There is a ruby-and-diamond necklace, a sapphire bracelet and other heirlooms. I don't know exactly all of them."

"What a pity." Zorah paused. Viola kept her breathing slow and easy.

"When is the next evening your employers will be away from home?"

"Tonight they will attend a musicale beginning at eight. They won't be home until well after midnight."

"What time do the servants retire?"

"After they have finished their duties."

More questions quickly followed about the servants' evening routine.

"Now, sleep. When I count to three you will awaken and you will not remember any questions about your employer or her jewellery. You will remember only that I counselled you about your lover. You will tell everyone who asks that I did nothing untoward. That I soothed your worries and questions. Understand?"

"Yes."

"Do you understand?"

Viola was on the verge of repeating her answer when she heard Miranda reply, "Yes."

"Good. Now one, two, and three . . ."

Viola blinked and opened her eyes.

The Gypsy smiled.

"So then, Miss Brown, have I taken care of your worries?"

"Oh, yes. I feel much better. All my worries seemed to have disappeared."

"Good. Now you must excuse me because I have another reading in ten minutes."

"She did seem eager to get rid of us, did she not?" Viola asked Miranda when they were once again on the street.

"Viola, how can you say so? Particularly after she comforted you."

Viola blinked and gazed more closely at Miranda. "What about her behaviour?"

"I saw nothing untoward in how she acted."

Alarums went off in Viola's brain. "You didn't gaze at the locket, did you, Miranda? Especially after warning me that we must not!"

Miranda's brow wrinkled. "What locket?" she asked.

"You *were* hypnotized!" Viola exclaimed. This was the outside of enough. She could just image the lightning bolts Avery would unleash on her head if he knew. She must make sure he never learned of it.

"Viola, I fear you are not speaking sensibly," Miranda said primly. "I wasn't hypnotized by any locket."

"Oh, no. Of course not. I am such a peagoose. Can you remember what happened in the back room? My memory is getting to be as abominable as Avery's."

Miranda smoothed a blond lock of hair over her ear. "Of course I remember. You asked the Gypsy questions about the problems you were experiencing being in love. I suppose you meant Richard. And I am relieved to say the Gypsy sees a happy future for you and him."

"You do not recall her asking me any other questions?"

"She supplied the answers, Viola, not the questions. I am happy that relations between you and Richard will be better soon."

To this cheerful remark Viola could make no reply.

"Shouldn't we hail a hack?" Miranda asked. "The wind is becoming chilly."

Obediently, Viola flagged down the driver of a hackney cab, and they were soon on their way to Berkeley Square. Viola tried to make sense of the past hour. If Miranda did not know what had transpired in the tea room, Viola could not ask her help in laying a trap for the thieves tonight. In fact, Miranda might be a real impediment to her plan for the evening.

It was just eleven when they got back to Berkeley Square and found Lord Newton staggering up the steps to the door with a huge bouquet of orchids.

"My lord, what are you doing here?" Miranda asked. "Isn't it time for your lesson at Jackson's?"

"I cancelled it this morning," he said, wiping his brow with a handkerchief. "These flowers are for you."

"Thank you. They are very pretty," Miranda said, giving them no more than a cursory look.

"They are more than pretty, Miranda," Viola chided, touching one of the delicate purple blooms. "They are quite beautiful and so exotic."

"You were out on some errands?" Newton next asked Miranda.

"We went to a Gypsy tea room and had a private reading."

Viola rued the impulse which had caused her to give in to Miranda's entreaties this morning.

"Oh?" Newton looked surprised by this answer. "A rather dangerous expedition."

"Fiddle. It wasn't in the least dangerous," Miranda said.

"Lord Newton is right, Miranda," Viola interjected swiftly. "It wasn't wise of me to take you to such a place. And I will not do so again. Please, my lord, oblige me by not mentioning it to Avery."

After winning Newton's reluctant consent to not say a word to his old friend, Viola asked if he were attending Lady Bingham's rout that evening.

"Will you be there?" he demanded.

"Yes."

"Well, perhaps I could change my schedule and attend, as well," Newton said quickly. "You will allow me a dance with you, Miss Symes?"

"If you wish one," she said with a shrug.

"Will you come in and have some refreshment?" Viola asked, recalled to her duties as a hostess and aware that they were still standing on the steps in front of her residence.

"Thank you," Newton said, stepping across the threshold with them.

"No lemonade for me," Miranda said. "I just remembered that Lord Carlisle wished to show me Richmond Park today. He promised to call at eleven. It is nearly that now. I must change."

Quickly Miranda skipped up the stairs, leaving a disappointed Newton in her wake.

"She is very young," Viola said later to Newton after she had changed quickly from Polly's brown dress and into an elegant cream-coloured muslin. She poured him a glass of Madeira in the drawing room.

He glanced up into her sympathetic eyes. "I believe she's two years your senior, Viola."

"Ah, well. I am very young, too."

"Yes, you are." He managed a laugh. "Do you think I am a fool to pursue Miranda when she has told you quite plainly that she has no partiality for me?"

"She said no such thing," Viola protested. "She is dotingly fond of you."

"Like an older brother. Have you ever heard of anything so quelling?"

"It is not what you wished to hear?"

He snorted. "I don't want her dotingly fond of me. I want her wildly in love with me."

Viola nearly spluttered on the Madeira. "Hadrian, I had no suspicion you were such a romantic."

He grimaced. "Nor I until last night when Avery told me at the club what Miranda thought of me. Blast it, I shall make her change her mind somehow. I spent all morning locating the orchids, and she spends two minutes looking at them and can only think of her Richmond Park outing with Carlisle."

"Will you take a suggestion?" Viola asked, remembering Miranda's wish for a man who would make her pulses race.

"About Miranda? Yes, gladly."

"Tonight at the Bingham party, let your true feelings for Miranda show."

"If I did I'd call Carlisle out!"

"I don't suggest you to go to that extreme," she said. "But you might show Miranda how much you admire her. Don't settle for a stuffy country dance when you could waltz with her. And if the circumstances should present themselves, I think you might gaze into her eyes and tell her you love her. You might even consider kissing her."

"Viola," he protested, much shocked. "Surely that's coming it too strong."

"Do you want her to marry Carlisle or some other sprig?"

"No, by Jove." He nodded. "Very well. I shall act like a dog in the manger and make it plain that I consider her mine." He paused and shook Viola's hand. "If I win her, I'll have you to thank."

"No thanks are necessary. Just do remember not to mention the Gypsy tea room to Avery."

"If you will promise me that is the last time you go there," he said, looking intently into her eyes.

"I promise," she said from the bottom of her heart. After tonight there would be no need to go back to the Gypsy tea room.

CHAPTER SIXTEEN

"IT IS TWELVE O'CLOCK, my lord."

Walter's words, although gently uttered, felt as if they had been trumpeted into Avery's ear. Shuddering, Richard held a hand to his forehead to keep his skull from reverberating.

"You did wish to be awakened at twelve, my lord."

"Did I? What a stupid request. Henceforth if I am addled enough to leave such an order, you are commanded to ignore it," Avery replied weakly.

"Yes, my lord."

The earl squinted through the fog of discomfort enveloping him. "And Walter—"

"My lord?"

"Be so good as not to shout when you answer me. You are not in the army."

"Very good, my lord." Walter hid a knowing smile.

Avery closed his eyes. "I remember when I was similarly afflicted years ago you cured me with a particularly potent tonic."

"It doesn't cure your headache, my lord," Walter demurred. "But it does make you feel more the thing."

"That's what I need," Avery snapped, then wished he hadn't because his head felt as if it had just bounced off his neck and against the wall. "I beg you mix the potion and bring it to me at once," he said with a wave of dismissal.

After the valet left, Avery lay back in his huge four-poster. Foxed. At his age. He hadn't been in such a painful condition since he'd reached his majority.

"Blast it!"

He winced. What a gudgeon to have drunk so many glasses of claret last night. What the deuce could he have been thinking of? Or was it what he *didn't* want to think of? Namely, Viola and Duvane in each other's arms.

Swearing, he kicked the bedcovers off, a move which jarred his aching head once again.

Would there be no peace for him today? Must he lie in bed like an invalid? With some difficulty, he ignored the malicious voice inside him which pointed out that all this brouhaha was entirely his own fault.

He swung his legs onto the floor and for one dizzying moment thought he would pitch forward. Then the room righted itself. It was in this position that Walter found him when he returned with the elixir he had just mixed.

"It tastes foul," Walter warned.

"I remember."

"And it smells foul, too."

"I can smell it from here," Avery growled. "Just give it to me quic'.ly."

Obligingly, Walter placed the silver cup in the earl's hands.

Avery held his breath and lifted the cup to his lips. Foul, Walter had warned, and so it was. The earl choked but swallowed it down manfully.

"Some water to wash it down, my lord." Walter took the empty cup away and deposited another in Avery's hands.

The earl gulped down the water.

"Where ever did you find this noxious mixture?"

"An old family recipe, my lord. It takes an hour to work. You will be feeling much more the thing. You could even be dancing before the day is over."

"All I wish to have is a quiet day and evening."

"Your appointment at Manton's?"

"Send James to cancel it."

The news of Avery's ailment reached Lady Avery's ears thanks to James, who met her belowstairs on his way out to Manton's. Wondering how ill Avery could be, Viola sought out Walter.

"Should I send for a physician?" she asked.

"His lordship merely had a touch of the headache from too much claret, my lady," Walter explained.

"I see," Viola said, relieved that Avery was not desperately ill. "Walter, has his lordship said anything about his plans for the evening?"

"He plans to spend a quiet evening at home."

"He's not serious!" Viola ejaculated.

"Too much racketing about he claims will make his headache worse."

Viola retreated to her bedchamber, her mind aflutter. Avery must not be allowed to spend a quiet evening at home tonight. She was expecting the thieves to break in. If Avery were present, they might be scared off or not even attempt the robbery. How like him to be an obstacle to the very plan which would set her free.

She bit her lower lip. Somehow, some way, she had to get him out of the house.

AVERY STARED DOWN at the cream-coloured note in his hand.

"Richard, please come to me. I shall be waiting in my bed. Viola."

For a moment he thought he was dreaming. He blinked hard, but no, the note was real enough. Viola was asking for him to come to her. At last!

Thank God for Walter's potion. His head no longer ached and he could put one foot in front of the other without toppling over. Zounds, it would have been a cruel fate if at the very moment Viola welcomed him into her arms he had not been able to acquit himself well.

But he had no fear of that. Already his heart was beating faster at the thought of being with Viola, at the taste of her mouth, at the softness of her breasts. He felt a tightening in his loins and resolutely turned his mind away from thoughts of Viola's physical charms. He didn't want to have the deed finished before ever he reached her chamber. After more than a year of marriage they would finally consummate their vows.

He crossed over to the looking-glass and stared hard at his reflection. Not too shabby a creature, he thought, smoothing his coat of Bath blue superfine and patting his cravat.

A minute later, he strode into the hallway and to the door of Viola's private rooms. He lifted his hand and knocked. The door opened, and Polly curtsied.

"Her ladyship is expecting you, my lord."

"You may leave us alone, Polly," he ordered.

Polly's eyebrows lifted, but mutely she did as he bade.

Avery walked through the dressing room. He glanced at the table with cosmetics, remembering his first night back in London when he had found Viola's wedding ring on that same table. All because she had carried a stupid asp in her reticule. Well, no longer. Not even an asp would keep him from her tonight.

"Viola?" he called out softly.

"I am in here, Richard."

He stepped eagerly in the direction of the voice. The gauzy draperies surrounding Viola's bed had been pulled back, and she reclined there, her large violet eyes looking larger than ever. Her face was pale. *Probably frightened, poor dear,* Avery thought as he laid a hand on her brow. He would take care that her pleasure exceeded any fear which she might have.

"Viola," he said huskily and kissed her forehead. His lips moved downward to a cheek.

"Richard, it was good of you to come so quickly."

"I have been waiting for your message a long time, sweet." He touched a forefinger to the tip of her nose and then kissed her.

Viola gasped as his lips touched hers. What was he doing! She had sent for him to ask him to take Miranda to the Bingham affair. She knew he might cut up stiff over it, so had prepared for his objection by pretending to be sick with the grippe. Apparently, her acting wasn't very good.

But his kissing certainly was, she thought as a weak sensation grew in the pit of her stomach. Perhaps she should cough, but how could she when she could scarcely breathe? What had come over him? His strong arms tightened around her, half lifting her out of the bed. He planted feverish kisses on her throat, at the same time murmuring soothing words.

"Richard..." She swallowed hard, before remembering that she should be coughing.

"Yes."

"I have something to ask you."

"Anything your heart desires."

"You may think it an odd request. Would you escort Miranda to the Bingham rout tonight?" she asked.

Whatever Avery had expected his wife to ask, it was not this, and he pulled away from her, nearly dropping her onto the bed.

"You see, Miranda is wild to go to the Binghams' and I have a mild case of the grippe," Viola said, taking her fences in a rush. "That's why I sent the message in to you just now."

"A mild case of the grippe," he said thickly. "That's why you wanted to see me."

"I am not contagious," she protested as he drew farther away. "But Polly thought it best that I rest in bed most of today and this evening."

"*That's* why you wrote that I would find you in bed," he said, fixing his gaze on her.

"Yes," she said at once. "Did you think it meant something else?"

He had no intention of revealing his misinterpretation to her. Straightening his cravat, he moved away.

"Will you do it, Richard?" she asked.

"Do what?" he replied irritably.

"Accompany Miranda to the Bingham rout."

"Oh, that. I certainly will not."

His curt reaction startled Viola. He had seemed so eager to please when he had first come into her bedchamber. She frowned. He couldn't have misread her message, could he?

"Please, Richard. I don't like to ask the favour of you, but it's for Miranda's sake."

"Miranda can miss one tiresome rout. You are not the only one feeling out of curl this afternoon."

"Yes, I know. I hope you are recovered."

"Barely," came his frigid reply.

"You seemed perfectly stout when you came in."

"I have exhausted what little energy I possessed getting from my bed to yours," he said dampeningly.

"Why, that's a hum. You certainly did not seem at all exhausted when you kissed me." She came to a stricken halt at his white-lipped glare. Perhaps it wasn't such a good idea to bring his kisses back to mind. "I already told Lord Newton that Miranda would be attending," she explained quickly.

"I don't want to hear another word about Hadrian. He kept me up most of the night discussing his idiotish plans to woo and win Miranda. I had to drink to keep from nodding off."

"But Newton is the very one for Miranda. You must see that we ought to assist him in his courtship of your cousin."

"I see nothing of the sort. Why must I accompany Miranda anywhere? If Hadrian is going to the rout, she can go with him."

"Not alone!" Viola said, much shocked. "Not without a female chaperon."

"I am not a female."

"No, but you are her cousin and she is staying with you. No one, not even a high stickler like Mrs. Drummond Burrel, can take exception to that. Say you'll do it, Avery, for Newton's sake."

"For Newton's sake," Avery muttered. "Oh, very well. I'll take Miranda to the wretched rout, but he'd better come up to scratch because I won't accompany her to any other affair, not even if the grippe keeps you in bed for a week!"

"Oh, it won't," Viola said with a smile. "I think I shall be feeling better by the morrow. In fact I am convinced of it."

"WHERE THE DEVIL was Hadrian? Avery scanned the thick of the crowd in the Bingham ballroom, searching for his friend. He had been roped into accompanying Miranda to this dreadful squeeze on the assumption that it would further Hadrian's cause and his friend—blast him!—was nowhere to be found in the crush. Had Lady Bingham invited all London to her tedious affair, or did it only seem that way, he wondered as he spied Captain Montgomery and Major Townshead striding purposefully across the room.

"Here come the cavalry," he murmured to Miranda as her admirers approached.

Within minutes, the two military gentlemen were cajoling Miranda for a dance. She stood on easy terms with them both, Avery noted. So easy that if Hadrian didn't arrive soon she might delude herself into falling in love with one of them.

Miranda stood up with the major for the quadrille and promised the captain a similar treat later, after he first escorted her into the refreshment room. Avery watched the flirting with a benevolent eye. He saw no reason to accompany the three of them. His stomach was better, but he still did not feel tempted to eat anything.

Lord Dixon paused in front of Avery.

"Sad crush, isn't it?" he asked.

The earl nodded.

"Not sampling the champagne tonight?"

"God, no!" Avery ejaculated. "I mean, very obliged to you but I'd as lief not." He wanted a good night's sleep and to be awakened without a splitting head-ache.

Dixon clapped him on the shoulder and laughed.

"I know the feeling, Richard. Believe me, I do know the feeling."

Avery moved away from Dixon, a tactical error be-cause Lady Brightly stepped immediately towards him. He could not retreat and so held his ground.

"Dear Lord Avery, so charmed to see you again so soon."

"Lady Brightly, I didn't know you were acquainted with the Binghams."

"Oh, I am a distant relation of Clara's. She was al-ways reluctant to acknowledge the connexion, but then the other day I paid a call on her and told her we had been invited to your ball. That took the wind out of her sails!"

"I'm sure it did," he said, wondering at the vulgar-ity of this woman. Fortunately, he glanced up and spied Newton at the door of the ballroom and made at once for his friend.

"Where the deuce have you been?" he declared by way of a greeting.

"Richard, what are *you* doing here?" Newton asked, looking amused.

"Playing chaperon."

"What? You're bosky."

"Viola took ill and couldn't accompany Miranda. I was pressed into service."

The twinkle in Newton's blue eyes grew more pronounced.

"A rare treat for you."

"Ungrateful cur. I hate squeezes like this."

"So do I. That explains my tardy entrance. Where is the fair Miranda?"

"Sharing lemonade with Montgomery and Townshead."

Newton frowned. "Rather lax chaperonage, my friend."

"She's perfectly safe. It's a ball. Besides, they are a pair of harmless pups. Not much competition for you."

A strange look came into Newton's eyes. "I hope that I shall not disappoint you, Richard," he said and marched off in the direction of the refreshment room.

Miranda was just about to bite into a lobster patty when she saw Newton striding into the room. Always a well-dressed gentleman, today he looked even more imposing than ever. His gaze skimmed the room until it met hers. A distinct jolt hit Miranda. How odd. She'd never before noticed that air of command about him. She felt a real sense of pleasure as he crossed immediately to her side. Would either the captain or the major look so handsome in regular evening dress, she mused.

"Hadrian, good fellow, how are you?"

Newton ignored the greeting from the captain and held out a hand to Miranda.

"I believe you promised me the next waltz, Miss Symes?"

"Now see here, Hadrian, you can't just come in and snatch her out of our hands," the major protested.

Newton's mouth lifted in amusement. "Oh, can't I?" he asked. "Just watch me."

With that he laced his fingers with Miranda's and tugged gently.

"Come," he commanded.

Miranda blinked. This was not the Newton she knew. That Newton generally uttered civil requests, not commands. She felt unable to resist the pull of his eyes. Without knowing exactly how or why, she rose to her feet and followed him to the ballroom.

He cupped her elbow and dropped his head to her ear.

"Let's have our waltz."

Her ear tingled from the warmth of his breath. They had waltzed before, but her legs trembled now as his hand clasped her waist.

"I don't remember promising you a waltz," she said.

"Yes, you did. You promised me every waltz tonight."

She looked up at his intent face. "You're roasting me."

He smiled. "I am perfectly serious. I plan to dance every waltz with you tonight and every quadrille."

"How absurd. You mustn't do that. What will people think? Besides, you can't," she said with a crow of laughter. "I already promised Montgomery a quadrille."

"Then I shall convey your regrets at having to break your promise to him."

Just what Miranda might have said to that was never to be known for another couple not as well schooled in the act of waltzing bumped into them during a turn. Newton's arm around Miranda tightened, and he stopped.

"Oh, I say, Hadrian, very sorry about that," the other gentleman apologized.

"See that it does not happen again!"

Miranda was baffled. Newton was usually the most amiable of souls. Nothing set him off. "It is all right, my lord. I am not hurt," she said.

"But you could have been." He stared at the back of the retreating couple. "I've had enough of waltzing."

"Yes, so have I," she agreed quickly. "Perhaps some fresh air. It is so warm in here."

"Come with me," he said, taking her by the hand and leading her out of the side door and onto the small terrace. "Is this better?"

"Oh, yes," she said, lifting her flushed face to the cooling breezes. But when she glanced at Newton, she felt that strange warmth suffuse her once again. A small pathway led down from the terrace to the statuary garden. They walked together, neither one saying very much.

"Who is this?" Miranda asked, pausing to peer more closely at a stone figure.

"Neptune," Newton said promptly. "You can tell by his trident and beard."

"And this one?"

"That is Venus, the goddess of love."

"Do you think her beautiful?" Miranda asked, walking round the statue.

"Not half as beautiful as you," he murmured.

Miranda turned. Newton's face loomed as large as a moon. It was Newton, and yet it wasn't. Then she had no time to think another thought because he was kissing her. A most unbrotherly kiss, she realized startled by the way his lips coaxed hers open. Her heart raced, and her hands twined themselves behind his neck. His arms crushed her to his chest as though he would never let her go.

"My lord," she said, when she could speak at last. "What are you doing?"

"Kissing you," he said shakily and lowered his mouth to hers again.

"But someone will see us."

"Let them. We're celebrating our betrothal."

"Our what!"

He held her off for a moment. "Marry me, Miranda. I love you."

"You love me?" she asked, feeling a sudden thrill within which grew even more pronounced when his eyes darkened with that rakish glint that caused her to feel like swooning.

"Will you marry me, minx?"

"What would you do if I said no?"

"Kiss you until you changed your mind," he said promptly, reaching for her again.

Ten minutes later, Lord Avery peered down from the terrace. He had seen Hadrian and Miranda leave the ballroom and thought it only proper to give his friend time to pop the question. But he was also aware that he had his own responsibilities to Miranda.

He walked down the stone pathway until he came to Bingham's stone statues. In the distance he saw a sculpture of two lovers entwined.

But the lovers were not stone, but flesh and blood, he discovered a moment later as the unmistakable sighs of ardour became audible. And not just any flesh and blood but Miranda and Newton. Well, well. She was not treating him like an older brother now, was she? With a broad grin, he stole back up to the terrace.

Now at last that was over and done with. And not a moment too soon. He could make his *adieux* post-haste and return home. He felt sure Viola was perishing to hear all about it.

CHAPTER SEVENTEEN

VIOLA PEERED OUT of her window at the dimly lit sky.
The moon was just a sliver hiding behind the billow-
ing clouds. Somewhere in the house the case clock
struck the hour. As the eleventh bong faded into silence, Viola could no longer mask her disappointment. No sign of the thieves. Had she made a mistake
in her planning? Perhaps the tea room had nothing to
do with the break-ins. On the other side of her bedchamber, James crouched and stifled a yawn, causing
the implacable Briggs standing close by to fix a baleful
eye on his underling.

"Don't fall asleep on us," he hissed.

"Not asleep," James said.

"We need to have our wits about us."

"My wits are in perfect order," the footman retorted.

Briggs glared at him. This was what resulted when
certain unworthy souls were paid more than their
rightful salary.

"Pray, don't quarrel," Viola called out. "I know this
waiting is intolerable, particularly with only the dying
embers of the fire to warm us." She rubbed her arms
briskly under the white muslin gown she wore.

"What time will his lordship be returning with Miss Miranda?" Briggs asked.

"I don't know," Viola replied. "With luck the party will last until one."

"Here now, stay awake, you..." Briggs caught James between nods and elbowed him sharply. The footman came awake on the instant, clutching the du-elling pistol in his lap.

"I've got him! I've got him!" he cried out.

"Stop it, fool. It's me!" Briggs said, breaking James's grasp easily while Viola ducked for cover. James continued to wave the pistol wildly.

Perhaps it hadn't been such a good idea to borrow the pistols from Avery's library, Viola thought. But the three of them needed a weapon. Viola hoped the pistols would frighten the thieves into surrendering.

She crept to the window and peered out again. The night was still very dark, but she caught a glimpse of a solitary figure approaching. With a sinking heart she recognized the person as Avery.

"Oh, heavens, it's Richard!" she exclaimed.

"What?" Briggs, busy browbeating James, stopped and cocked his head at her.

"It's his lordship. He's come back from the ball, but without Miranda. How peculiar!"

"What shall we do?" James asked.

"Nothing. I told him before he left that I was going to give the servants the night off. He was surprised but he didn't argue with me. He will probably go to bed himself or to his library."

"He might ring for us," James pointed out.

"Let us pray he does not," Viola answered.

Upon entering his residence, Avery was surprised to find no one about. His first impulse was to summon Briggs, then he remembered. Briggs had the night off. The earl shrugged out of his coat and picked up a forgotten walking-stick resting on the table in the hallway. He took the stairs two at a time, swinging the cane and thinking of Newton and Miranda's wedding to come. Viola would no doubt want to hear how the ball went.

Impetuously, he rapped on her door with the cane.

"Viola?" he called out softly.

Inside the bedroom, Viola froze at the sound of Avery's voice. She exchanged an agonized look with Briggs.

"What shall we do, my lady?" he whispered.

"I'd better answer. You stay here, and keep an eye out for the robbers."

She went through the dressing room to the door.

The knocking grew louder.

"Where is Polly?" Avery asked when Viola finally opened the door to him.

"Asleep. She was feeling unwell."

Polly had actually been outraged that her mistress intended to keep a vigil in the bedchamber with the two male servants, putting up such a commotion that Viola had been at last obliged to tell her everything about the trap for the thieves. This had led to a fresh round of the vapours before Polly had been carried off, clutching a vinaigrette.

"May I come in?" Avery asked.

She had no choice but to stand aside and let him enter.

"I shan't stay long. I just thought you might want the full particulars about Newton and Miranda."

"Newton and Miranda?"

Avery stared at her. Her complexion was even paler than usual. "You did send me out this evening to further their courtship, did you not?" he asked.

"Oh, yes, Newton and Miranda. Pray excuse me, Avery, but I was drifting into sleep when you knocked."

"My apologies. The good news is Miranda no longer looks upon Newton as an older brother. In fact she was enjoying an ardent exchange of kisses with him. I'll go bail we shall soon be wishing her happy."

"Splendid!" Viola said, pleased with this successful turn of events. "Where is she?"

"I left them back in Bingham's statuary garden. I didn't think they should be disturbed. Presumably, Newton will escort her home."

An idea took root in Viola's mind. "Perhaps you should go back and try to find them, sir. They may be worried about where you disappeared to."

He laughed aloud. "What an absurd notion." Then his laughter faded into a frown. Why was she so eager to have him leave?

He eyed her closely. "You seem much recovered from your illness."

"Such is often the case with the grippe," she murmured.

"Why did you give the servants the night off?" he asked softly.

She picked up a perfume bottle from her dressing-table. "They deserve it."

"Perhaps. Had you some special reason to get me out of the house and the servants out of your way?"

If he only knew that two servants were very much in the way, standing not ten yards from them, Viola thought as she applied the scent to her earlobe. Why couldn't he have stayed at the soirée an hour longer? It would have saved her from having to explain things to him.

"You are not alone in these rooms, are you madam?" Avery asked, his face now a study in anger. "My apologies for coming home too early as well as for my curiosity. I'm compelled to put a face to the man who has cuckolded me."

"Cuckolded you!" The perfume bottle slipped from Viola's hand and crashed to the floor, spilling out its lavender scent. "Avery!"

He paid no attention to her words nor to the stain spreading on the rug. Two long strides took him to the wardrobe. He threw wide the doors, finding nothing within except silks and satins.

"Is the blackguard still warming your bed?" he asked, turning on his heel and making for the bed. He jabbed his cane viciously at the goose-down mattress. "Where is he?"

Then he heard movement in the corner.

His eyes gleamed as he spotted the draperies moving ever so slightly. "Just like in *Hamlet*."

"Avery no, really. You mustn't think—"

"Don't fall into a pucker, my dear. I wield a cane, not a sword." So saying he thumped the drapery with two solid blows.

A howl went up. Smiling, the earl parted the draperies and reached a hand in to drag out Duvane. What he pulled out instead was his butler.

"Briggs!" he thundered.

"Good evening, my lord," Briggs murmured, holding a hand to a cut on his forehead.

"Oh, Briggs, are you very hurt?" Viola asked. "I tried to stop him, but he was too fast."

Avery's eyes swivelled from his butler's face to his wife's. What was Briggs doing here? And where the devil was Duvane? Viola wouldn't be cavorting with Briggs, or would she? No. That was an idiotish idea.

"I had no notion you were behind the drape, Briggs," he said. "Have you sustained a serious injury?"

"No, my lord. Your stick caught me only a glancing blow."

"Where is James?" Viola asked.

"In the corner," spoke the footman.

Feeling as though he were in the midst of one of Mr. Sheridan's comedies, Avery whirled around. James stepped out from the shadows. First Briggs. Now James. What was Viola up to? And where was Duvane?

"I shall fetch a salve for that cut," Viola told Briggs and bustled into her dressing room. Avery was right on her heels.

"A moment, if you please," he ordered. "I demand to know just what my footman and butler were doing in your private rooms at this hour of the night."

"It should be obvious. They were cuckolding you!"

"Viola!" he said, incensed. "I see nothing funny in such a declaration."

"Well, I thought that's what you were attempting to do—find my paramour!"

"Just what were my footman and butler doing in your private rooms, madam?" he repeated.

"Helping me with a household matter," she said, improvising quickly. Her nose wrinkled against the strong odour of lavender permeating the air.

"What household matter?" he asked sceptically.

"Really, Avery, how unfeeling of you to play the inquisitor now when Briggs is bleeding. I must get something to stop it."

"Take this," he said, handing her a handkerchief. "It will make a suitable compress."

"But this is the finest linen. Walter will have a fit if we ruin it. I shall find something suitable for a bandage."

"The handkerchief will do."

"I shall need water," she said, going over to the basin.

"My lady, come!" James whispered from the bedchamber.

Quickly she crossed to him. "Is it Briggs?"

"No! It's the one we've been waiting for."

"At last!"

"Who is this? What is going on? Who have you been waiting for?" Avery thundered, following her in.

"Hush!" Viola threw the command over her shoulder. "If you can't be quiet, then go to your room."

He couldn't believe his ears. *"What!"*

"My lady, they will be here any minute."

"Get down!" she ordered, and yanked Avery down to his knees in the corner.

Crouched in the darkness, the earl pondered the painful reality of a wife gone mad. He would have to confine her to Bedlam where he could visit her weekly.

"Briggs went to the window and heard noises," James said in a hush.

The drape stirred momentarily as the butler took his place again behind it.

"What is going on?" Avery asked again. He would not be hushed. He had every right to know what this havy-cavy business was. He was the master of his own home, wasn't he?

"Do be still," Viola commanded. "Are you ready, James?"

"Aye, as ready as I'll ever be."

The seconds crawled past. Avery sat cross-legged on the floor and wondered what any of his tonnish friends would say if they could see him.

A tree branch hit the window. The skin on his neck stood up. Not exactly a tree branch. The window was being opened. Avery could see Viola's face inches away. Excitement glittered in her eyes.

Then he heard the sound of someone stealthily climbing into the room. Avery felt his own muscles tense.

Footsteps hurried towards the bed.

"Painting, do you see a painting?" a voice asked.

"Over the bed, she said."

Viola lay perfectly flat, not daring to breathe. James, sitting nearby, waited, alert for her signal.

The two thieves stood on her bed, lifting up the heavy painting.

"Now!" Viola exclaimed.

With a roar, James dashed towards the bed. But as quickly as he moved, he was a full stop behind the earl who had sprinted forward to tackle one of the pair lifting the painting.

"That's the way! That's the way!" Briggs exhorted, emerging from the draperies and brandishing the duelling pistol. The thieves had no time to be intimidated by a weapon neither of them could really see. The thief Avery had tackled was already crawling towards the door. The earl pinnioned him. The thief grappling with James had the heavy framed picture in his hands and was trying to crown the footman with it. Fearing more injury to her servants, Viola snatched up Avery's walking-stick and felled the culprit with a solid blow. He dropped the picture of Avery's mother on the floor and toppled next to it.

"You weren't supposed to be here," he protested.

"Lights!" Avery shouted.

Briggs hastened to light the candles in the room. Avery surveyed the clandestine callers. One cowered on the bed while the other lay near the door. Any fight in them disappeared when Briggs approached, holding the duelling pistol.

"Briggs, how is your head?" Viola demanded.

"The bleeding has stopped, my lady."

"Good. Do you feel up to finding a place to hold these two until James goes to Bow Street and alerts the Runners?"

"I have the perfect place for them, my lady," Briggs said.

"Was that my duelling pistol?" Avery asked after the servants had taken the two men away.

"Yes, you don't mind, do you?" Viola asked. "We didn't shoot it. We didn't even load it."

Avery laid a hand on each of her shoulders and turned her gently to face him.

"Viola, do you think you could tell me now what this is all about?" he asked.

"It was about the thieves and the reward for their capture, of course. Dorothea told me about the Rose Garden tea room. A Gypsy does private readings for governesses there. I thought she might be involved. So I went for a visit and laid a trap."

"You could have been hurt!" he protested.

"No, that's why I enlisted James and Briggs's help."

"You could have told me what was afoot." He stroked his chin.

She lifted hers. "Would you have approved?"

"Probably not."

"Definitely not," she corrected. "You would have ordered me to abandon my attempts to capture the thieves."

"Why were you so determined to capture them?"

"Because of the reward, silly. It's more than a thousand pounds."

Avery's indulgent mood vanished. Once again Viola's avaricious streak had surfaced. "Does the money mean so much to you?" he asked with a trace of hauteur in his voice.

"It means the world to me!" she exclaimed. It meant her freedom and the assurance that she would have a roof over her head when they were divorced. But how could she explain that to him? She would not dare.

So his wife was not satisfied with the pin money and the lavish clothes and home she had. She needed more. Avery straightened his shoulders. She was destined to be a purse-squeeze who always yearned for more.

"Do you still wish a divorce?" he asked abruptly.

She glanced up, startled. The question had come like a bolt out of the blue.

"Answer me." His face was set in such stern lines that she could not help but look away.

"Yes, of course, I want the divorce."

"So be it."

He turned and walked out of the room. Viola watched him go, feeling curiously bereft. She ought to have been happy. She had done the thing and captured the thieves and could claim the reward of more than a thousand pounds. Now Avery had as good as given her her freedom. It was what she wanted. Then why did she feel so wretched, she demanded as she flung herself down on the bed and began to weep.

THE NEXT MORNING while Avery enjoyed a solitary cup of coffee in the breakfast parlour, a footman arrived with a letter from Lord Newton.

With a feeling of foreboding, the earl broke the seal and attempted to decipher the muddy hand of his childhood friend.

"Richard, I am on my way to Gretna Green with Miranda. Hadrian."

This was followed by a postscript of thanks from Miranda for allowing her to stay at Berkeley Square.

Avery say back in his chair. An elopement, by Jove. When Viola came in for breakfast he was still sitting, staring at the letter from Newton. Quickly, he handed it to her and watched her face turn the colour of her ivory day dress.

"But this must be a joke! One of Newton's pranks," she protested.

Avery shook his head. "No such thing. Not the sort of stuff Hadrian would kick up a lark about. Take it from me, they'll be married when we lay eyes on them again."

"Heavens what a coil!"

"I think not. It's eminently suitable. Miranda is of age and I have half a suspicion it was her idea."

Viola smiled. "She did wish a gentleman who would sweep her off her feet. Such a romantic idea." She gave her head a shake, recalling another matter which must be addressed. "What about the grand ball for her? Ought we to cancel it?

Avery waved a careless hand. "Do as you wish. A cancellation would probably be wisest. Once the news of the elopement and our impending divorce gets about, we won't any of us feel in the mood for festivities."

"You are probably right," she said, troubled that he seemed to consider the divorce a *fait accompli.*

"Bow Street has already informed me that the thieves have made a full confession to the robberies. As you suspected, they implicated that Gypsy woman. She received a third of the ill-got gains. The reward will be transferred to the bank of your choice." He rose from the table.

"Are you leaving so soon? You've barely eaten."

"I have an early appointment," he said.

Probably with his *chère amie,* Viola thought. Left alone, she began to eat, but found the food unpalatable. She was still toying with a wedge of cheese half an hour later when Briggs led Dorothea and Susan into the room.

"Odious of us to just descend on you this way!" Dorothea exclaimed. "But we had to know everything about the thieves' capture."

"Do you mean you have already heard the news?"

"One of my footmen saw your James leading the culprits down to Bow Street this morning," Susan revealed, undoing the strings of her straw hat.

"How did you capture them?" Dorothea asked, accepting a cup of coffee from Viola.

Quickly, Viola explained about the Gypsy tea room and her visit with Miranda to set a trap for the culprits.

"So it *was* that Gypsy tea room. Why did I never think to visit it?" Dorothea asked.

"Perhaps because you were not seeking employment as a governess," Viola answered with a smile.

Susan choked on the scone she was nibbling. "Governess! What nonsense is this?"

"I have tried to convince her to give up this silly plan but without success, Susan. You are welcome to try your best," Dorothea invited.

"Avery and I are petitioning for a divorce, Susan," Viola said quickly before Susan could unleash a barrage of questions. "I know your dislike of any scandal in the family. But I beg you to think of our happiness. We are so wretchedly unhappy together. To divorce seems only sensible."

"Do you mean to say my brother accepted this idea with equanimity?"

"Not at all," she admitted. "But last night he told me he would agree."

"What a pudding-heart!"

"Oh, he's no such thing!" Viola exclaimed. "If you could have seen him last night leaping at the thieves with no thought to his personal safety. He's the bravest man I know." This impassioned defence of her husband's mettle caused Dorothea and Susan to exchange speaking looks.

"Heroic, indeed," Dorothea murmured, stirring cream, which she never used, into her coffee.

"I beg your ladyship's pardon," Briggs said from the doorway, "but Lord Carlisle has called. Something about an early morning drive with Miss Miranda."

"Oh, heavens, Briggs, you must fob him off. Make up some excuse. Anything."

"Miranda is not seeing Carlisle?" Dorothea asked after the butler left to deal with the caller.

"Miranda is on her way to Gretna Green with Newton," Viola confided, seeing no reason not to share this titbit with her friends. "We received a letter this morning from Lord Newton saying that he was heading for the Border with Miranda."

"Good God, I never dreamed Hadrian was such a romantic!" Dorothea exclaimed.

"But what about the ball?" Susan wailed.

"I don't know. Avery thinks we should cancel it."

"What a pity. After all the work you put into it."

"Why not hold the ball?" Dorothea interjected. "Not for Miranda but for you and Avery. If you are both agreed to your plans to divorce, then you should enjoy one last event as host and hostess."

"But, Viola, you mustn't get a divorce," Susan pleaded. "I know Richard's hardly a paragon as a husband, but since he's come back I had hoped that you two would make up."

"You are good to think that. I, too, had originally nursed hopes, but no longer. Avery has set up a mistress at Albemarle Street. He is probably on his way to her now," she said with a forlorn smile.

CHAPTER EIGHTEEN

AVERY'S EARLY-MORNING appointment was not with Miss Garda as Viola feared, but with Peter Thacker. When their bill of divorcement came to pass, the earl intended to provide for Viola. He had no wish to see her destitute.

With this plan in mind, he stepped into Mr. Thacker's office and found his solicitor staring dreamily out the window, oblivious to the stack of papers on his desk.

"How now, Peter, wool-gathering?" the earl quizzed.

Mr. Thacker turned round and nearly toppled out of his chair. "Oh, Lord Avery. Do come in."

Avery seated himself and dealt an indulgent smile at the other man.

"It is too lovely a day to be confined, is it not?"

"I can explain, sir."

Avery smiled. "You need not say a word."

Au contraire, Mr. Thacker thought as he squared his bony shoulders. He had a good deal to explain to the earl, particularly about seeing Miss Garda five times in the past week. Mr. Thacker had never been in love before, but he knew himself to be seriously fixing an interest in Lord Avery's friend from India. What was even more exhilarating, she seemed to return his regard. Mr. Thacker drew in a breath. He had dreaded this interview, but he owed it to Neelah to see it through.

"I'm here to ask your assistance on a personal matter, Peter," Avery said.

"You are?" the lawyer asked distractedly.

"Yes. It concerns a woman you have grown fond of, I believe." Avery managed a weak smile. He had not forgotten Thacker's affection for Viola.

Mr. Thacker stiffened with alarm. How had the earl learned of his relationship with Miss Garda? Of course a man of his rank could learn anything if he applied himself.

"It's a sticky business," Avery continued, gazing fixedly at the wall behind Thacker. "But I've reached the conclusion that she and I no longer suit."

"You don't!" Mr. Thacker exclaimed with such force that the earl was startled.

"No, I don't, that is, we don't. I wish to be generous to her after we part. Draw up something in the way of settlement, won't you?"

Mr. Thacker felt as though a great weight had been lifted off his shoulders.

"That won't be necessary, my lord."

"I know it's not *necessary,* Peter," Avery said, an expression of annoyance flitting into his eyes momentarily, "but I want to do it. She thinks me an ogre, but I'll do this for her if nothing else."

"If you will allow me a moment's indulgence, sir," Mr. Thacker said. "First, let me assure you that there is not the slightest need to provide a settlement."

"You are looking at it from a legal perspective," Avery said.

"No, my lord, a purely personal one. I shall take great delight in providing for the lady."

"You shall *what?*" Avery thundered, rising from his chair and looming over the desk until he was nose to nose with Mr. Thacker.

"I know you probably think it very bad of me, but I couldn't help falling in love with her!" Thacker said, opening his budget completely. "And what seems more incredible is she has fallen in love with me."

All colour drained from the earl's face, leaving him nearly as white as his shirt-front. He sank back in his chair. "Good God."

Mr. Thacker accepted this reaction with surprising equanimity. "I mean to marry her as soon as I can. I know there will be delays. We must all follow legal procedures. But my intentions are honourable."

"How fortunate for you." The earl spoke through gritted teeth. Viola and his man of business? "May I enquire how long this has been going on?"

"About a fortnight."

"Only a fortnight?" Avery quizzed. "I would have suspected it began earlier when she nursed you through your illness."

Mr. Thacker's brow creased. "Illness? Nothing of the sort." His words faltered. "My lord," he said aghast. "You mustn't think I am in love with Lady Avery!"

Avery scowled. "Why not? You have just confessed to it."

Mr. Thacker swallowed so hard that his Adam's apple bobbed up and down. "I am not in love with your wife, my lord. I am in love with your mistress."

"What mistress?" Avery roared, rising from his chair.

"Miss Garda!"

"She's not my mistress," he said irritably. "Never touched the woman." He drew himself up ramrod straight. "Do you mean you were referring all this time to Miss Garda?" he demanded. "You want to marry *her?*"

"Yes. I confess I have quite lost my heart to her."

Mr. Thacker thereupon embarked on an enthusiastic history of his courtship of Miss Garda. Avery was too suffused with relief that Thacker and Viola were not romantically entangled to put a stop to the litany of praise pouring from the solicitor's lips.

An hour later, he managed to extricate himself from Thacker's office. He had still not given his lawyer the details of the settlement he wished to bestow on Viola. Quite clearly, Peter was preoccupied at the moment and wouldn't remember any instructions given to him for at least a sennight.

As Avery mulled over what would constitute an appropriate wedding gift for his lawyer, he noticed Mr. Challerton walking jauntily down the street and postponed climbing immediately into his high-perch phaeton.

"Good day, Mr. Challerton," he called out.

"Ah, good day, Avery. Much obliged to you for that cheque you sent round. It's cleared a good portion of the debt I owe."

"Does that account for your good cheer?"

Viola's father laughed. "Not entirely." He looked over his shoulder and then lowered his voice into a conspiratorial whisper. "I daresay you haven't heard the news about Duvane? He and young Talbot met this morning at Paddington Green."

"Good Jupiter, why?"

"Duvane was caught at the table with a card up his sleeve. Talbot called him on the cheat and Duvane demanded satisfaction. Well, he got it."

"Killed?" Avery demanded.

Mr. Challerton shook his head regretfully. "No, not killed. But Duvane won't be dancing on that leg anytime soon. Probably won't even be able to go to that ball of yours."

"How did you know he received an invitation to our ball?" Avery asked.

Mr. Challerton chuckled. "I wrangled it for him. I owed the fellow a considerable sum. He told me he'd forgive the debt if an invitation was sent to him. Viola obliged me by doing so. I hope it didn't cause too much trouble between the two of you."

Avery shrugged. "Things are going so badly between us that it hardly matters any more. I should warn you that you and I shall not be related for much longer, sir.''

The older man nodded. "Viola told me what she had in mind. I'm surprised that you consented to so idiotish a scheme."

The earl was not offended by such plain talk. "She desires it."

"The chit doesn't know what she wants," Mr. Challerton scoffed. "Over a year ago, the only thing she wanted was you."

Avery's lip curled. "She wanted my fortune."

"No, *I* wanted your fortune," Challerton said with no hint of embarrassment on his childlike face. "No sense peeling eggs with you. I've been in Dun Territory for years. But you weren't the only sprig after my daughter. You weren't even the first eligible on my list, if truth be told. Bantry offered for her, and he has style and address and is dotingly kind, and his pockets are even deeper than yours."

"A pity Viola didn't know that," Avery said drily.

"Oh, she did!" Challerton averred. "I made sure of that. As her father I pointed out all the advantages of the match."

His son-in-law frowned. "You told her that Bantry had more money than I?"

"Certainly. I wanted her to accept him. He would be a dashed sight easier to coax money from than you. But she wouldn't hear of it. The chit was in love with you."

"But on our wedding day I distinctly heard her agree with her aunt that my fortune was the main attraction. Not a word about love passed her lips."

"Oh, bosh! If she's talking to her aunt Viola would agree to be the Queen of Siam. She never could abide that awful woman. Neither can I. Countless times I would come into the sitting room to see Viola with a smile plastered on her face, nodding her head like a simpleton and saying, 'Yes, Aunt. I quite agree with you.'"

"Are you telling me the truth?" Avery demanded, much struck by this image, which summed up perfectly how Viola had looked in the drawing room with her aunt on their wedding day.

"Why would I lie about such a thing?" Viola's father retorted.

"If Bantry was so much richer than I, why did you accept my offer?"

Mr. Challerton looked thoroughly disgusted.

"Because she wanted you! Haven't you been listening? She turned up her nose at Bantry and anyone else. Stormed about how she loved you and wanted only you as her husband. Vowed to turn into an ape leader otherwise. Well, I couldn't have that. Not as deep in the suds as I was. I apologize if that's a blow to your esteem, my lord."

"No offence taken, Challerton." Avery held out his hand. "In fact you don't know how pleased I am to hear that I was your second choice."

Avery drove his Welshbreds back to Berkeley Square at breakneck speed. Viola had married him out of love, not greed. He should have known. He should never have doubted her.

"Where is my wife?" he asked Briggs, slamming the door to his residence shut after him.

The butler looked startled. "Lady Avery is in the blue drawing room with Lady Susan and Lady Dixon. They are discussing a theatrical to be held at the Dixons'."

Avery was already taking the stairs two at a time, his mind set on only one thing. Viola. He threw open the doors to the blue drawing room, blind to the charming tableau the three occupants on the couch made as they huddled over a quarto of Mr. Shakespeare's plays. In an effort to coax Viola out of the dismals, Dorothea had decided that she would hold a theatrical at her residence shortly.

The first to notice Avery was his sister. Lady Susan rose majestically. "Richard," she began.

Avery had learned from his previous two encounters with his sister and sidestepped her, going immediately to Viola and swinging her up into his arms.

"Avery, what are you doing!" Viola exclaimed at finding herself crushed against his strong chest.

Instead of answering, he carried her from the drawing room.

"Stop it this instant. Do you hear? Put me down," she ordered breathlessly. She could scarcely speak, she was clasped so tightly in his arms.

Avery crossed the hall and stepped into the library. He kicked the door shut after them and placed Viola down on the sofa.

"Have you lost your wits?" she gasped.

"If I have, it's your fault," he replied, leaning over her and kissing her forehead. "Hear me out, Viola, before you wish me to Jericho. I must ask you a question. Answer me truthfully. Why did you marry me?"

"Good God, I have oft-times wondered that myself!" she blurted out.

He sat down next to her and seized her hands in his. "Why did you marry me?" he repeated.

His eyes were so blue they reminded her of the sea off Brighton.

"Why did you ask me?" she countered, looking away.

He cupped her chin in his hand.

"I have just come from a tête-à-tête with your father, who informed me that you ranted and raved to him, declaring that I was the only man you wanted to wed. Is that true?"

"How like Papa to remember such a thing now."

His finger stroked her jawline gently. "I am obliged to him for the excellence of his memory. Indeed I stand considerably in his debt. So much so that he may hang on my sleeve for the rest of his life."

"Good heavens, really?" Viola was utterly amazed. How had her husband and father got to be at first oars with each other?

"You wanted to marry me. You turned down an offer from Lord Bantry, did you not?" he asked.

"What if I did?"

"Why?" he asked.

Viola found herself wishing he were not seated so close to her.

"Why?" she echoed.

"Bantry has higher rank than I and is deeper in the pocket. Why me?"

"Why you?" The anger in her eyes softened. "Because I was daft for you then. I loved you, Richard," she acknowledged. Fool that she was. She glanced down at the Wilton carpet.

"I love you, too, sweet."

His words caused a shiver to dance down the length of her spine.

She looked up at him.

"No, you don't," she said, holding up her hands as though to ward off a blow. "How can you? You fled on our wedding day."

He seized her hands and pressed his lips to them. "I do love you. I loved you so much, even though my foolish pride had suffered a blow. I thought you didn't love me. I chanced to overhear your conversation with your aunt on our wedding day. I thought you'd married me just for the size of my purse."

"How could you think that!" she said, too shocked to notice that he was planting feverish kisses on her palms. "What conversation with my aunt?" she asked. "Oh, heavens, do you mean that dreadful interview? From that you deduced I was a fortune-hunter?"

He nodded. "I was so struck to the core that I fled rather than confront you." He grimaced. "I wanted to be loved for myself. But I couldn't tell anyone that, especially not you, since I believed you didn't love me. I couldn't tolerate your laughing at my romantic notions. Much easier to sail off to India. Forgive me. I have lost a whole year with you."

His lips were drawing precipitously closer to hers when she suddenly remembered his *chère amie*.

"Why did you install a *chère amie* at Albemarle Street?" she demanded. She might still love him, but she had to know the truth.

"I have no *chère amie* at Albemarle Street," he said.

"Avery, I saw the bill for the employment of servants there."

"The lady who currently resides at Albemarle Street is going to marry Mr. Thacker."

"Mr. Thacker!"

"Yes. I shall explain more fully about her later. Right now I think it high time that I acted like a husband." He pulled her into his arms and gazed deeply into her violet eyes. When his mouth bent down to meet hers, Viola felt her heart race. A sensation of warmth grew in the pit of her stomach, leaving her weak-kneed.

"There will be no divorce between us," he murmured huskily against her hair. "Do you hear?" He kissed her again.

"But you told me last night you wanted one," she pointed out, nestling closer against his coat of Bath blue superfine.

"I don't care what I said last night. It is not the prerogative of your sex alone to change your minds. We males may do likewise." He dropped a kiss on her head. "No divorce. Not now. Not ever."

He punctuated each word with another lingering kiss.

Several enjoyable minutes passed before Avery grew conscious of someone pounding on the door to his library.

"Go away!" he shouted.

"Richard, let me in."

Avery gazed helplessly down at his wife in his arms. "Susan," he said with accents of loathing.

"You'd best open the door," Viola said, suppressing a giggle.

Reluctantly, he obeyed.

Lady Susan stood, eyes blazing with fury and ready to do battle with her brother. But Richard held his ground.

"Richard, what is going on?" she demanded.

"Go away, Sue."

"I will not allow you to do violence to Viola," she warned, prepared to launch herself through the narrow opening of the door.

"I was not doing violence to Viola. I was kissing her."

"Oh? *Oh!*" The anxiety cleared from his sister's eyes. "Good! I always knew you couldn't be such a slowtop."

"Thank you. Very civil of you."

"This means the divorce is off, I hope?"

"Certainly. We can't have any scandal in the family. But I warn you if you don't let me return to the library, I shall murder you and then the quizzes will talk!" He closed the door firmly in her face. "Now where were we, my dear?" Avery asked, turning again to Viola who held out her arms to him.

"Richard, tell me the truth. Are you so afraid of scandal if we divorced?" she asked some minutes later.

"Certainly. But I fear something more."

"Which is?"

"Losing you again."

"Again? You never lost me, Richard. Not even when you returned and were quite odious to me."

He felt a stab of remorse. "I beg pardon. I was odious, but it was because I thought you loved Duvane."

"Duvane! How could you? He was pleasant and amusing, but he never ever could hold a candle to you," she spoke with such passion that he had to smile.

"You composed that musical piece for him," he said.

"I composed it for you! I wrote it because I missed you so much. I was just embarrassed to tell you so. A lady does not wear her heart on her sleeve."

"Nor does a gentleman," he countered. "Oh, Viola, we've lost an entire year," he said with real regret. "I wanted to show you things. Susan has taught you all about the ton. Dorothea has even taught you how to drive in the city."

"There is one thing I have not learned, my lord," she said shyly.

"Which is?" He cocked an inquisitive eye her way.

"How a wife may please a husband in bed," she said. "I hope you don't think it too forward of me, but I own to a certain curiosity. Could we have the first lesson soon?"

"I think we could comply with such a request," he said with a grin. "How would immediately suit you?" he asked, and swung her up in his arms once again.